RTI

Speech & Language Interventions
for the
Regular Classroom Teacher
Speech & Language Interventions Any Teacher Can Use!

- **Research Based**

- **Step by Step Instructions for Implementation**

- **Language Processing Interventions**

  - Following one and two-step oral directions

  - Answering 'wh' questions

- **Articulation Interventions**

- **Includes Data Point Assessment Sheets**

Written and Illustrated by
Dr. Sherri Dobbs Santos

ISBN# 978-0-578-00321-4

Contact Dr. Sherri Dobbs Santos at: sherrisantos229@comcast.net

Table of Contents

What is RTI?

Response to Intervention (RTI) is a multi-tier approach to the early identification and support of students with learning and behavior needs. The RTI process begins with high-quality instruction and universal screening of all children in the general education classroom. Struggling learners are provided with interventions at increasing levels of intensity to accelerate their rate of learning. These services may be provided by a variety of personnel, including general education teachers, special educators, and specialists. Progress is closely monitored to assess both the learning rate and level of performance of individual students. Educational decisions about the intensity and duration of interventions are based on individual student response to instruction. RTI is designed for use when making decisions in both general education and special education, creating a well-integrated system of instruction and intervention guided by child outcome data. (National Center for Learning Disabilities, 2008)

How can Speech & Language Interventions Help?

Students with language processing and/or articulation problems can benefit from repeated practice in the area(s) in which they struggle. This manual includes interventions to address both language processing and speech articulation problems. Interventions included in this manual are specifically designed to help those students who have been unsuccessful with regular classroom instruction (Tier I in the RTI model) and/or small group instruction (Tier II in the RTI model). These interventions are geared to target specific skills in which the child is lacking and to provide the student with immediate feedback and reinforcement to strengthen those skills (Tier III in the RTI model). Weekly assessments are an integral part to these interventions. Monitoring of the student's progress throughout the implementation period (between 6 to 12 weeks) is critical to assess both the effectiveness of the intervention and the student's response to that intervention. This manual includes data point recording sheets to help the teacher/tutor document the student's RTI and to determine if new interventions are needed or if a full speech language evaluation by a speech language pathologist is needed.

INTERVENTION

Targeted Skill: Speech Language

Name of Intervention: Following One-Step Oral Directions

Description of Intervention: Student is given a series of one-step directions to follow on a daily basis to improve receptive language/processing skills.

Procedures for Implementing the Intervention:
STEP ONE: Teacher/tutor tells student that he/she will work on following one-step directions.
STEP TWO: Teacher/tutor states a one-step direction to the student. If student follows the direction correctly, move on to a second one-step direction until a total of 10 one-step directions have been given. If the student does not follow the direction correctly, repeat the direction. If after repeating the direction the student still doesn't follow the direction, model the correct response.
Optional technique: Have the student repeat back the direction before he/she attempts to follow it.
STEP THREE: On a weekly basis assess how well the student follows one-step directions using the "Speech Language Assessment Checklist: Following One-Step Directions".

Assessment That Can be Used to Monitor Progress: Speech Language Assessment Checklist: Following One-Step Directions

Research References:
Austin, J. L., & Agar, G. (2005). Helping Young Children Follow Their Teachers' Directions: The Utility of High Probability Command Sequences in Pre-K and Kindergarten Classrooms. *Education & Treatment of Children, 28*(3), 222+.
Glover, J. A. (1987). Oral Directions: Remembering What to Do When. *Journal of Educational Research, 81*(1), 33-40.

Student Name: _____ Grade: _____ Teacher/Tutor: _____

Speech Language Assessment Checklist
"Following One-Step Directions"

<u>Directions</u>: Ask the student each one-step direction and mark (+) for correct responses and (-) for incorrect responses. (BL= Baseline, DP = Data Point)

	BL	DP# 1	DP# 2	DP# 3	DP# 4	DP# 5	DP# 6	DP# 7	DP# 8
Date:	_____	_____	_____	_____	_____	_____	_____	_____	_____
1. Touch your nose.									
2. Jump up three times.									
3. Clap your hands.									
4. Stomp your feet.									
5. Point to a person.									
6. Stand on one foot.									
7. Smile.									
8. Count to 10.									
9. Pick up a pencil.									
10. Blink your eyes three times.									

Comments:

_____
_____
_____
_____
_____
_____
_____
_____
_____
_____
_____
_____
_____

INTERVENTION

Targeted Skill: Speech Language

Name of Intervention: Following Two-Step Oral Directions

Description of Intervention: Student is given a series of two-step directions to follow on a daily basis to improve receptive language/processing skills.

Procedures for Implementing the Intervention:

STEP ONE: Teacher/tutor tells student that he/she will work on following two-step directions.

STEP TWO: Teacher/tutor states a two-step direction to the student. If student follows the direction correctly, move on to a second two-step direction until a total of 10 two-step directions have been given. If the student does not follow the direction correctly, repeat the direction. If after repeating the direction the student still doesn't follow the direction, model the correct response.

Optional technique: Have the student repeat back the direction before he/she attempts to follow it.

STEP THREE: On a weekly basis assess how well the student follows two-step directions using the "Speech Language Assessment Checklist: Following Two-Step Directions".

Assessment That Can be Used to Monitor Progress: Speech Language Assessment Checklist: Following Two-Step Directions

Research References:

Austin, J. L., & Agar, G. (2005). Helping Young Children Follow Their Teachers' Directions: The Utility of High Probability Command Sequences in Pre-K and Kindergarten Classrooms. *Education & Treatment of Children, 28*(3), 222+.

Glover, J. A. (1987). Oral Directions: Remembering What to Do When. *Journal of Educational Research, 81*(1), 33-40.

Student Name: _____ Grade: _____ Teacher/Tutor: _____

Speech Language Assessment Checklist
"Following Two-Step Directions"

Directions: Ask the student each two-step direction and mark (+) for correct responses and (-) for incorrect responses. (BL= Baseline, DP = Data Point)

	BL	DP# 1	DP# 2	DP# 3	DP# 4	DP# 5	DP# 6	DP# 7	DP# 8
Date:	____	____	____	____	____	____	____	____	____
1. Blink your eyes twice and then touch your nose.									
2. Turn around once and then hop on one foot.									
3. Pick up a pencil and bring it to me.									
4. Point to a chair and then go sit in it.									
5. Smile real big and then clap your hands three times.									
6. Touch your toes and then count to 10.									
7. Take two steps forward and then turn around two times.									
8. Go find a book and then open it to the last page.									
9. Pat your stomach four times and then say your name.									
10. Raise your hands in the air and then hum a song.									

Comments:

_____

_____

_____

_____

_____

_____

INTERVENTION

Targeted Skill: Speech Language

Name of Intervention: Answering 'Who' Questions

Description of Intervention: Student is asked a series of 'Who' questions on a daily basis to improve language/processing skills.

Procedures for Implementing the Intervention:
STEP ONE: Teacher/tutor tells student that he/she will work on answering 'Who' questions.
STEP TWO: Teacher/tutor asks the student 10 random 'Who' questions. If student gives an incorrect response, tutor models the correct response and has student repeat.
STEP THREE: Teacher/tutor monitors the student's progress by assessing the student's ability to answer 'Who' questions correctly. Teacher/tutor records responses on "Speech Language Assessment Checklist: Who Questions"

Assessment That Can be Used to Monitor Progress: Speech Language Assessment Checklist "Who Questions"

Research References:
Berninger, V. W., Abbott, R. D., Vermuelen, K., Ogier, S., Brooksher, R., Zook, D., et al. (2002). Comparison of Faster and Slower Responders to Early Intervention in Reading: Differentiating Features of Their Language Profiles. *Learning Disability Quarterly, 25*(1), 59+.

Justice, L. M., Kaderavek, J., Bowles, R., & Grimm, K. (2005). Language Impairment, Parent-Child Shared Reading, and Phonological Awareness: A Feasibility Study. *Topics in Early Childhood Special Education, 25*(3), 143+.

Lindsay, G., & Dockrell, J. E. (2004). Whose Job Is It? Parents' Concerns about the Needs of Their Children with Language Problems. *Journal of Special Education, 37*(4), 225+.

Ram, A. (1991). A Theory of Questions and Question Asking. *Journal of the Learning Sciences, 1*(3 & 4), 273-318.

Student Name: _____ Grade: _____ Teacher/Tutor: _____

Speech Language Assessment Checklist
"Who Questions"

<u>Directions</u>: Ask the student each 'Who' question and mark (+) for correct responses and (-) for incorrect responses. (BL= Baseline, DP = Data Point)

	BL	DP# 1	DP# 2	DP# 3	DP# 4	DP# 5	DP# 6	DP# 7	DP# 8
Date:	_____	_____	_____	_____	_____	_____	_____	_____	_____
1. Who is the leader of the school? *The principal*									
2. Who teaches you at school? *Teacher*									
3. The President lives in the White House. Who lives in the White House? *The President*									
4. Who brings you food at a restaurant? *The waiter/waitress*									
5. Who flies the airplane when you go on a trip? *The pilot*									
6. Who takes care of you at home? *Mom/dad/ grandmother/etc.*									
7. Brenda touched the hot stove. Who touched the hot stove? *Brenda*									
8. Who do you go to when you need a haircut? *Barber/ hairdresser*									
9. Who cooks the food at a restaurant? *Cook/chef*									
10. Who brings mail to your house every day? *The mailman/mail carrier*									

Comments:

_____

_____

_____

_____

_____

INTERVENTION

Speech Language
Answering 'What' Questions

Targeted Skill: Speech Language

Name of Intervention: Answering 'What' Questions

Description of Intervention: Student is asked a series of 'What' questions on a daily basis to improve language/processing skills.

Procedures for Implementing the Intervention:
STEP ONE: Teacher/tutor tells student that he/she will work on answering 'What' questions.
STEP TWO: Teacher/tutor asks the student 10 random 'What' questions. If student gives an incorrect response, tutor models the correct response and has student repeat.
STEP THREE: Teacher/tutor monitors the student's progress by assessing the student's ability to answer 'What' questions correctly. Teacher/tutor records responses on " Speech Language Assessment Checklist: What Questions"

Assessment That Can be Used to Monitor Progress: Speech Language Assessment Checklist "What Questions"

Research References:
Berninger, V. W., Abbott, R. D., Vermuelen, K., Ogier, S., Brooksher, R., Zook, D., et al. (2002). Comparison of Faster and Slower Responders to Early Intervention in Reading: Differentiating Features of Their Language Profiles. *Learning Disability Quarterly, 25*(1), 59+.

Justice, L. M., Kaderavek, J., Bowles, R., & Grimm, K. (2005). Language Impairment, Parent-Child Shared Reading, and Phonological Awareness: A Feasibility Study. *Topics in Early Childhood Special Education, 25*(3), 143+.

Lindsay, G., & Dockrell, J. E. (2004). Whose Job Is It? Parents' Concerns about the Needs of Their Children with Language Problems. *Journal of Special Education, 37*(4), 225+.

Ram, A. (1991). A Theory of Questions and Question Asking. *Journal of the Learning Sciences, 1*(3 & 4), 273-318.

Student Name: _____ Grade: _____ Teacher/Tutor: _____

Speech Language Assessment Checklist
"What Questions"

<u>Directions</u>: Ask the student each 'What' question and mark (+) for correct responses and (-) for incorrect responses. (BL= Baseline, DP = Data Point)

	BL	DP# 1	DP# 2	DP# 3	DP# 4	DP# 5	DP# 6	DP# 7	DP# 8
Date:	____	____	____	____	____	____	____	____	____
1. What do you do with a spoon? *You eat with it.*									
2. What do you do with a shoe? *Put it on your foot.*									
3. What do we eat at a birthday party? *Cake*									
4. What drink do we get from a cow? *Milk*									
5. Jeremy listens to the radio in the car. What does Jeremy listen to in the car? *The radio.*									
6. What do you do with a toothbrush? *You brush your teeth.*									
7. Last night we went to the movies. What did we do last night? *We went to the movies.*									
8. What does a bird build? *A nest.*									
9. What happens to the grass when it rains? *The grass gets wet, the grass grows.*									
10. What do you do when the telephone rings? *You answer it.*									

Comments:

_____

_____

_____

_____

_____

_____

_____

INTERVENTION

Targeted Skill: Speech Language

Name of Intervention: Answering 'When' Questions

Description of Intervention: Student is asked a series of 'When' questions on a daily basis to improve language/processing skills.

Procedures for Implementing the Intervention:
STEP ONE: Teacher/tutor tells student that he/she will work on answering 'When' questions.
STEP TWO: Teacher/tutor asks the student 10 random 'When' questions. If student gives an incorrect response, tutor models the correct response and has student repeat.
STEP THREE: Teacher/tutor monitors the student's progress by assessing the student's ability to answer 'When' questions correctly. Teacher/tutor records responses on " Speech Language Assessment Checklist: When Questions"

Assessment That Can be Used to Monitor Progress: Speech Language Assessment Checklist "When Questions"

Research References:
Berninger, V. W., Abbott, R. D., Vermuelen, K., Ogier, S., Brooksher, R., Zook, D., et al. (2002). Comparison of Faster and Slower Responders to Early Intervention in Reading: Differentiating Features of Their Language Profiles. *Learning Disability Quarterly, 25*(1), 59+.

Justice, L. M., Kaderavek, J., Bowles, R., & Grimm, K. (2005). Language Impairment, Parent-Child Shared Reading, and Phonological Awareness: A Feasibility Study. *Topics in Early Childhood Special Education, 25*(3), 143+.

Lindsay, G., & Dockrell, J. E. (2004). Whose Job Is It? Parents' Concerns about the Needs of Their Children with Language Problems. *Journal of Special Education, 37*(4), 225+.

Ram, A. (1991). A Theory of Questions and Question Asking. *Journal of the Learning Sciences, 1*(3 & 4), 273-318.

Student Name: _____ Grade: _____ Teacher/Tutor: _____

Speech Language Assessment Checklist
"When Questions"

<u>Directions</u>: Ask the student each 'When' question and mark (+) for correct responses and (-) for incorrect responses. (BL= Baseline, DP = Data Point)

	BL	DP# 1	DP# 2	DP# 3	DP# 4	DP# 5	DP# 6	DP# 7	DP# 8
Date:	_____	_____	_____	_____	_____	_____	_____	_____	_____
1. When do you go to bed? *At night/when it gets dark*									
2. When do you go to the doctor? *When you get sick/hurt/need shots/need a checkup.*									
3. Carl went to work this morning. When did Carl go to work? *This morning*									
4. When do you go to school? *In the morning/Monday, Tuesday, etc ...*									
5. When does it snow? *In the wintertime/when it's cold/at Christmas time*									
6. Debbie goes shopping every Friday. When does Debbie go shopping? *Every Friday*									
7. The game starts at 7:00. When does the game start? *At 7:00*									
8. When does the moon come out? *At night*									
9. When do roosters crow? *In the morning*									
10. Jamar has a dentist appointment at 2:30. When is Jamar's dentist appointment? *At 2:30*									

Comments:

_____

_____

_____

INTERVENTION

Speech Language
Answering 'Where' Questions

Targeted Skill: Speech Language

Name of Intervention: Answering 'Where' Questions

Description of Intervention: Student is asked a series of 'Where' questions on a daily basis to improve language/processing skills.

Procedures for Implementing the Intervention:
STEP ONE: Teacher/tutor tells student that he/she will work on answering 'Where' questions.
STEP TWO: Teacher/tutor asks the student 10 random 'Where' questions. If student gives an incorrect response, tutor models the correct response and has student repeat.
STEP THREE: Teacher/tutor monitors the student's progress by assessing the student's ability to answer 'Where' questions correctly. Teacher/tutor records responses on " Speech Language Assessment Checklist: Where Questions"

Assessment That Can be Used to Monitor Progress: Speech Language Assessment Checklist "Where Questions"

Research References:
Berninger, V. W., Abbott, R. D., Vermuelen, K., Ogier, S., Brooksher, R., Zook, D., et al. (2002). Comparison of Faster and Slower Responders to Early Intervention in Reading: Differentiating Features of Their Language Profiles. *Learning Disability Quarterly, 25*(1), 59+.

Justice, L. M., Kaderavek, J., Bowles, R., & Grimm, K. (2005). Language Impairment, Parent-Child Shared Reading, and Phonological Awareness: A Feasibility Study. *Topics in Early Childhood Special Education, 25*(3), 143+.

Lindsay, G., & Dockrell, J. E. (2004). Whose Job Is It? Parents' Concerns about the Needs of Their Children with Language Problems. *Journal of Special Education, 37*(4), 225+.

Ram, A. (1991). A Theory of Questions and Question Asking. *Journal of the Learning Sciences, 1*(3 & 4), 273-318.

Student Name: _____ Grade: _____ Teacher/Tutor: _____

Speech Language Assessment Checklist
"Where Questions"

<u>Directions</u>: Ask the student each 'Where' question and mark (+) for correct responses and (-) for incorrect responses. (BL= Baseline, DP = Data Point)

	BL	DP# 1	DP# 2	DP# 3	DP# 4	DP# 5	DP# 6	DP# 7	DP# 8
Date:	____	____	____	____	____	____	____	____	____
1. Today Toby's class went on a field trip to the zoo. Where did Toby's class go? *The zoo*									
2. Where do we wear socks? *On our feet*									
3. Where do you see clouds? *In the sky*									
4. Where do you get ice for a drink? *From the freezer/refrigerator*									
5. Sue's dad left to go to work. Where did Sue's dad go? *To work*									
6. Where do we go to see a movie? *Movie theater*									
7. Jim's dog likes to sleep on the sofa. Where does Jim's dog like to sleep? *On the sofa*									
8. Where do you go if you break your leg? *Hospital; Doctor's office*									
9. Where do you go to have your teeth cleaned? *Dentist's office*									
10. Where do you go to learn? *School*									

Comments:

_____

_____

_____

_____

_____

INTERVENTION

Targeted Skill: Speech Language

Name of Intervention: Answering 'Why' Questions

Description of Intervention: Student is asked a series of 'Why' questions on a daily basis to improve language/processing skills.

Procedures for Implementing the Intervention:
STEP ONE: Teacher/tutor tells student that he/she will work on answering 'Why' questions.
STEP TWO: Teacher/tutor asks the student 10 random 'Why' questions. If student gives an incorrect response, tutor models the correct response and has student repeat.
STEP THREE: Teacher/tutor monitors the student's progress by assessing the student's ability to answer 'Why' questions correctly. Teacher/tutor records responses on " Speech Language Assessment Checklist: Why Questions"

Assessment That Can be Used to Monitor Progress: Speech Language Assessment Checklist "Why Questions"

Research References:
Berninger, V. W., Abbott, R. D., Vermuelen, K., Ogier, S., Brooksher, R., Zook, D., et al. (2002). Comparison of Faster and Slower Responders to Early Intervention in Reading: Differentiating Features of Their Language Profiles. *Learning Disability Quarterly, 25*(1), 59+.

Justice, L. M., Kaderavek, J., Bowles, R., & Grimm, K. (2005). Language Impairment, Parent-Child Shared Reading, and Phonological Awareness: A Feasibility Study. *Topics in Early Childhood Special Education, 25*(3), 143+.

Lindsay, G., & Dockrell, J. E. (2004). Whose Job Is It? Parents' Concerns about the Needs of Their Children with Language Problems. *Journal of Special Education, 37*(4), 225+.

Ram, A. (1991). A Theory of Questions and Question Asking. *Journal of the Learning Sciences, 1*(3 & 4), 273-318.

Student Name: _____ Grade: _____ Teacher/Tutor: _____

Speech Language Assessment Checklist
"Why Questions"

<u>Directions</u>: Ask the student each 'Why' question and mark (+) for correct responses and (-) for incorrect responses. (BL= Baseline, DP = Data Point)

	BL	DP# 1	DP# 2	DP# 3	DP# 4	DP# 5	DP# 6	DP# 7	DP# 8
Date:	_____	_____	_____	_____	_____	_____	_____	_____	_____
1. Why do children go to school? *To learn*									
2. Why do adults go to work? *To earn money/to pay for things/etc.*									
3. Why are tires round? *So that they will roll*									
4. Why do babies cry? *To tell us they are hungry/ hurt/wet/ etc.*									
5. Why do we brush our teeth? *To clean them/ to get rid of germs/to make them white/so we don't have cavities/ etc.*									
6. Why do we put locks on doors? *To keep robbers out/to protect our things/etc.*									
7. Why do ladies carry purses? *To hold their things/etc.*									
8. Why do we have bookshelves? *To have a place to put books.*									
9. Why do tables have four legs and not two? *So that it will stand up.*									
10. Freddie uses crutches because he broke his foot. Why does Freddie use crutches? *Because he has a broken foot.*									

Comments:

_____

_____

_____

_____

INTERVENTION

Targeted Skill: Speech Language

Name of Intervention: Answering 'How' Questions

Description of Intervention: Student is asked a series of 'How' questions on a daily basis to improve language/processing skills.

Procedures for Implementing the Intervention:
STEP ONE: Teacher/tutor tells student that he/she will work on answering 'How' questions.
STEP TWO: Teacher/tutor asks the student 10 random 'How' questions. If student gives an incorrect response, tutor models the correct response and has student repeat.
STEP THREE: Teacher/tutor monitors the student's progress by assessing the student's ability to answer 'How' questions correctly. Teacher/tutor records responses on " Speech Language Assessment Checklist: How Questions"

Assessment That Can be Used to Monitor Progress: Speech Language Assessment Checklist "How Questions"

Research References:
Berninger, V. W., Abbott, R. D., Vermuelen, K., Ogier, S., Brooksher, R., Zook, D., et al. (2002). Comparison of Faster and Slower Responders to Early Intervention in Reading: Differentiating Features of Their Language Profiles. *Learning Disability Quarterly, 25*(1), 59+.

Justice, L. M., Kaderavek, J., Bowles, R., & Grimm, K. (2005). Language Impairment, Parent-Child Shared Reading, and Phonological Awareness: A Feasibility Study. *Topics in Early Childhood Special Education, 25*(3), 143+.

Lindsay, G., & Dockrell, J. E. (2004). Whose Job Is It? Parents' Concerns about the Needs of Their Children with Language Problems. *Journal of Special Education, 37*(4), 225+.

Ram, A. (1991). A Theory of Questions and Question Asking. *Journal of the Learning Sciences, 1*(3 & 4), 273-318.

Student Name: _____ Grade: _____ Teacher/Tutor: _____

Speech Language Assessment Checklist
"How Questions"

Directions: Ask the student each 'How' question and mark (+) for correct responses and (-) for incorrect responses. (BL= Baseline, DP = Data Point)

	BL	DP# 1	DP# 2	DP# 3	DP# 4	DP# 5	DP# 6	DP# 7	DP# 8
Date:	____	____	____	____	____	____	____	____	____
1. How do you fix a sandwich? *Accept any logical answer*									
2. How do birds travel? *They fly*									
3. How do people protect themselves from the cold? *They wear a coat/ wrap up in a blanket/ stand next to a fire/ etc.*									
4. How do we dry off after we take a bath? *We use a towel to dry up the water on our bodies.*									
5. How do you unlock a door? *You use a key*									
6. How do people earn money? *They work/ they have a job/ etc.*									
7. How can doctors help us? *They help us get better when we are sick/ they give us medicine/ etc.*									
8. How do we eat soup? *With a spoon.*									
9. How do you put on socks? *Accept any logical answer*									
10. How do people talk to each other when they live far apart? *Phone calls/emails/letters/etc.*									

Comments:

_____

_____

_____

INTERVENTION

Speech Articulation

Targeted Skill: Speech Articulation

Targeted Grade Level: K-5

Name of Intervention: Speech Sound Practice

Description of Intervention: Student practices mispronounced speech sounds with a teacher or tutor.

Procedures for Implementing the Intervention:
STEP 1: Teacher/SLP identifies focus sound(s) and uses a picture sheet, a word list, or sentences to practice the sound with the student on a daily basis.
STEP 2: Each day ask the student to say the words with strong sound pronunciation. If the student does not correct the sound, provide a model by repeating the word. If the student still does not correct the sound, don't require repetition move on to the next word. If the student easily corrects the sounds, ask him/her to use some words in phrases or sentences, using strong sound pronunciation.
STEP 3: Monitor progress by recording responses on a word list or picture sheet. It is recommended that the student be assessed once weekly for a period of six weeks.
**ALTERNATIVE METHOD:**
The student practices the target sound(s) with a peer for 5 minutes each day. Both partners take turns saying words and sentences with the target sound speaking slowly and clearly. Both students provide feedback to the partner after each word is said.

Assessments That Can be Used to Monitor Progress: Articulation Drill Sheets

1. Initial R	33. Medial SH	65. Medial D
2. Medial R	34. Final SH	66. Final D
3. Final R	35. Initial CH	67. Initial J
4. Initial BR	36. Medial CH	68. Medial J
5. Initial DR	37. Final CH	69. Final J
6. Initial FR	38. Initial TH (voiceless)	70. Initial H
7. Initial GR	39. Initial TH (voiced)	71. Medial H
8. Initial KR	40. Medial TH (voiceless)	72. Final H
9. Initial PR	41. Medial TH (voiced)	73. Initial M
10. Initial TR	42. Final TH (voiceless)	74. Medial M
11. Initial S	43. Initial F	75. Final M
12. Medial S	44. Medial F	76. Initial N
13. Final S	45. Final F	77. Medial N
14. Initial SK	46. Initial V	78. Final N
15. Initial SL	47. Medial V	79. Initial Y
16. Initial SM	48. Final V	80. Medial Y
17. Initial SN	49. Initial K	
18. Initial SP	50. Medial K	
19. Initial ST	51. Final K	
20. Initial SW	52. Initial G	
21. Initial Z	53. Medial G	
22. Medial Z	54. Final G	
23. Final Z	55. Initial P	
24. Initial L	56. Medial P	
25. Medial L	57. Final P	
26. Final L	58. Initial B	
27. Initial BL	59. Medial B	
28. Initial FL	60. Final B	
29. Initial GL	61. Initial T	
30. Initial KL	62. Medial T	
31. Initial PL	63. Final T	
32. Initial SH	64. Initial D	

Research References:

Gillum, H., Camarata, S., Nelson, K. E., & Camarata, M. N. (2003). A Comparison of Naturalistic and Analog Treatment Effects in Children with Expressive Language Disorder and Poor Preintervention Imitation Skills. *Journal of Positive Behavior Interventions, 5*(3), 171+.

Justice, L. M., Kaderavek, J., Bowles, R., & Grimm, K. (2005). Language Impairment, Parent-Child Shared Reading, and Phonological Awareness: A Feasibility Study. *Topics in Early Childhood Special Education, 25*(3), 143+.

Justice, L. M., & Pence, K. L. (2004). Addressing the Language and Literacy Needs of Vulnerable Children: Innovative Strategies in the Context of Evidence-Based Practice. *Communication Disorders Quarterly, 25*(4), 173+.

Justice, L. M., & Pullen, P. C. (2003). Promising Interventions for Promoting Emergent Literacy Skills: Three Evidence-Based Approaches. *Topics in Early Childhood Special Education, 23*(3), 99+.

Lane, K. L., Pierson, M. R., Robertson, E. J., & Little, A. (2004). Teachers' Views of Prereferral Interventions: Perceptions of and Recommendations for Implementation Support. *Education & Treatment of Children, 27*(4), 420+.

Masterson, Julie J., & Perrey, Christine D. (1999). Research: Training Analogical Reasoning Skills In Children With Language Disorders. *American Journal of Speech Language Pathology, 8*, 58 - 61.

O'Connor, R. E., Notari-Syverson, A., & Vadasy, P. F. (1996). Ladders to Literacy: The Effects of Teacher-Led Phonological Activities for Kindergarten Children with and without Disabilities. *Exceptional Children, 63*(1), 117+.

Directions: Teacher says each word or sentence aloud to student and student repeats. If student states the word incorrectly, teacher restates the word and student repeats once more. Practice on the target sound should take place at least 3 times per week for a period of no less than six weeks. Assessments should be given once a week throughout the implementation period.

Directions for giving assessments: Once a week use this sheet to asses the student's ability to pronounce the target sound. For each correct response place a '+' in the box below or adjacent to the word or sentence. For each incorrect response place a '−' in the box.

Articulation Drill Sheet
Focus Sound "R"

Initial 'R' Words:

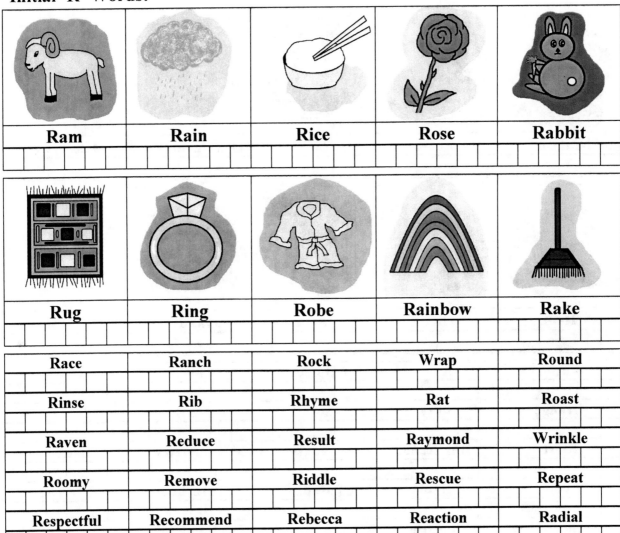

Ram	Rain	Rice	Rose	Rabbit

Rug	Ring	Robe	Rainbow	Rake

Race	Ranch	Rock	Wrap	Round
Rinse	Rib	Rhyme	Rat	Roast
Raven	Reduce	Result	Raymond	Wrinkle
Roomy	Remove	Riddle	Rescue	Repeat
Respectful	Recommend	Rebecca	Reaction	Radial

1. Last night I saw a <u>r</u>accoon.
2. At school I must follow the <u>r</u>ules.
3. I like to listen to the <u>r</u>adio.
4. I eat <u>r</u>aisins with my cereal.
5. She <u>r</u>ipped her jacket.
6. He is a <u>r</u>esponsible boy.
7. I will <u>r</u>elax at the beach.
8. I am <u>r</u>eady to go.
9. My mother has <u>r</u>ed shoes.
10. I saw the <u>r</u>ocket go high.

Record below the dates of each Data Point (DP):
DP #1 _____   DP #2 _____   DP #3 _____   DP #4 _____   DP #5 _____   DP #6 _____

Student Name: _____ Grade: _____ Teacher/Tutor: _____

Articulation Drill Sheet
Focus Sound "R"

Medial 'R' Words:

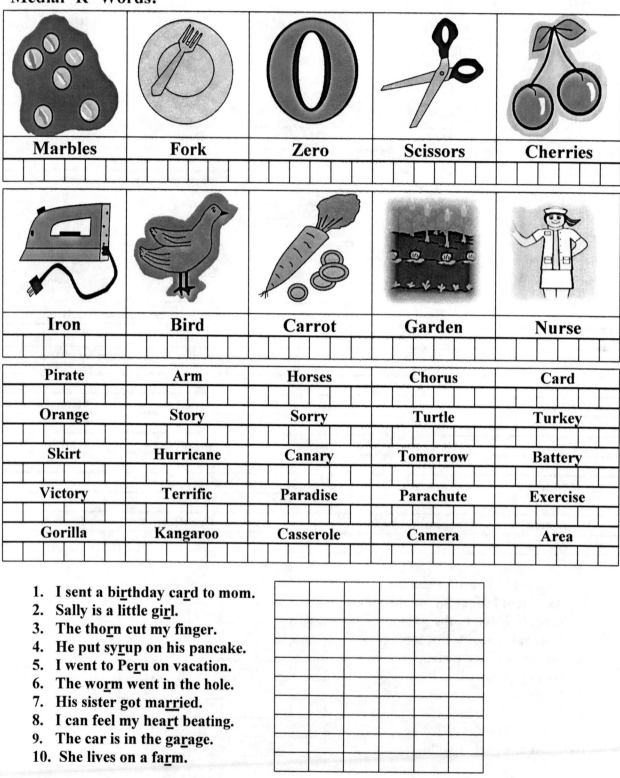

| Marbles | Fork | Zero | Scissors | Cherries |
| Iron | Bird | Carrot | Garden | Nurse |

Pirate	Arm	Horses	Chorus	Card
Orange	Story	Sorry	Turtle	Turkey
Skirt	Hurricane	Canary	Tomorrow	Battery
Victory	Terrific	Paradise	Parachute	Exercise
Gorilla	Kangaroo	Casserole	Camera	Area

1. I sent a birthday card to mom.
2. Sally is a little girl.
3. The thorn cut my finger.
4. He put syrup on his pancake.
5. I went to Peru on vacation.
6. The worm went in the hole.
7. His sister got married.
8. I can feel my heart beating.
9. The car is in the garage.
10. She lives on a farm.

Record below the dates of each Data Point (DP):
DP #1 _____ DP #2 _____ DP #3 _____ DP #4 _____ DP #5 _____ DP #6 _____

Student Name: _____ Grade: _____ Teacher/Tutor: _____

Directions: Teacher says each word or sentence aloud to student and student repeats. If student states the word incorrectly, teacher restates the word and student repeats once more. Practice on the target sound should take place at least 3 times per week for a period of no less than six weeks. Assessments should be given once a week throughout the implementation period.

Directions for giving assessments: Once a week use this sheet to asses the student's ability to pronounce the target sound. For each correct response place a '+' in the box below or adjacent to the word or sentence. For each incorrect response place a '−' in the box.

Articulation Drill Sheet
Focus Sound "R"

Final 'R' Words:

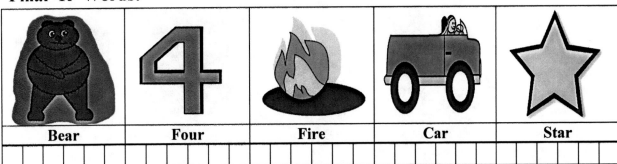

Bear	Four	Fire	Car	Star

Tire	Tiger	Pear	Tear	Teacher

Hammer	Letter	Mother	Panther	Shower

Spider	Ladder	Sugar	Hair	Square

Jar	Ear	Doctor	Rooster	Zipper

Sister	Dollar	Pepper	Feather	Swimmer

Newspaper	Juggler	Wheelchair	Shoulder	Alligator

1. I will cheer for the team.
2. My mom paid the cashier.
3. Please close the door.
4. Are you sure you want to go?
5. The sailor is on the boat.
6. Happy New Year!
7. Are you ready?
8. The painter dropped his brush.
9. The book is over there.
10. I admire my grandmother.

Record below the dates of each Data Point (DP):

DP #1 _____ DP #2 _____ DP #3 _____ DP #4 _____ DP #5 _____ DP #6 _____

27

Directions: Teacher says each word or sentence aloud to student and student repeats. If student states the word incorrectly, teacher restates the word and student repeats once more. Practice on the target sound should take place at least 3 times per week for a period of no less than six weeks. Assessments should be given once a week throughout the implementation period.

Directions for giving assessments: Once a week use this sheet to asses the student's ability to pronounce the target sound. For each correct response place a '+' in the box below or adjacent to the word or sentence. For each incorrect response place a '–' in the box.

Articulation Drill Sheet
Focus Sound "BR"

Initial 'BR' Words:

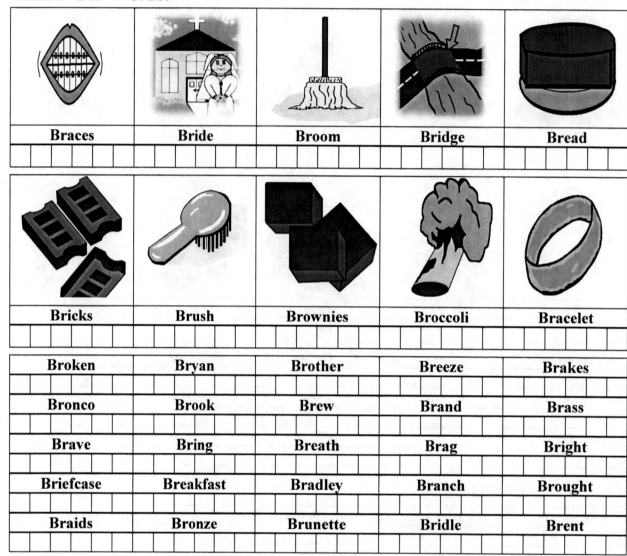

Braces	Bride	Broom	Bridge	Bread

Bricks	Brush	Brownies	Broccoli	Bracelet

Broken	Bryan	Brother	Breeze	Brakes
Bronco	Brook	Brew	Brand	Brass
Brave	Bring	Breath	Brag	Bright
Briefcase	Breakfast	Bradley	Branch	Brought
Braids	Bronze	Brunette	Bridle	Brent

1. My mom can walk <u>br</u>iskly.
2. He can read <u>Br</u>aille.
3. Her bones are <u>br</u>ittle.
4. We screamed "<u>Br</u>avo" at the concert.
5. The <u>br</u>own puppy licked my face.
6. <u>Br</u>enda is my best friend.
7. I tripped over the <u>br</u>oomstick.
8. She asked me to be her <u>br</u>idesmaid.
9. I <u>br</u>eathe hard after I run.
10. His father's name is <u>Br</u>uce.

Record below the dates of each Data Point (DP):

DP #1 _____ DP #2 _____ DP #3 _____ DP #4 _____ DP #5 _____ DP #6 _____

Student Name: _____ Grade: _____ Teacher/Tutor: _____

Articulation Drill Sheet
Focus Sound "DR"

Initial 'DR' Words:

Drum	Drink	Dragon	Dress	Drive
Drill	Drapes	Draw	Dryer	Dream

Drip	Drag	Dread	Dresser	Drastic
Drop	Drugstore	Dreary	Drab	Drool
Drift	Drank	Dramatic	Driveway	Dracula
Drown	Drain	Drench	Drawbridge	Dragonfly
Drumstick	Driven	Droop	Drawer	Droplet

1. He **dragged** his blanket on the floor.
2. The water went down the **drainpipe**.
3. My mom gets my medicine from the **druggist**.
4. The **drum** major led the band.
5. Today was a **dreary** day.
6. The baby is **drooling**.
7. She **drew** a beautiful picture.
8. My sweater is in the **dresser**.
9. They went to the **dry-cleaner**.
10. He is watching a **drama** on TV.

Record below the dates of each Data Point (DP):
DP #1 _____ DP #2 _____ DP #3 _____ DP #4 _____ DP #5 _____ DP #6 _____

29

Student Name: _____ Grade: _____ Teacher/Tutor: _____

Directions: Teacher says each word or sentence aloud to student and student repeats. If student states the word incorrectly, teacher restates the word and student repeats once more. Practice on the target sound should take place at least 3 times per week for a period of no less than six weeks. Assessments should be given once a week throughout the implementation period.
Directions for giving assessments: Once a week use this sheet to asses the student's ability to pronounce the target sound. For each correct response place a '+' in the box below or adjacent to the word or sentence. For each incorrect response place a '−' in the box.

Articulation Drill Sheet
Focus Sound "FR"

Initial 'FR' Words:

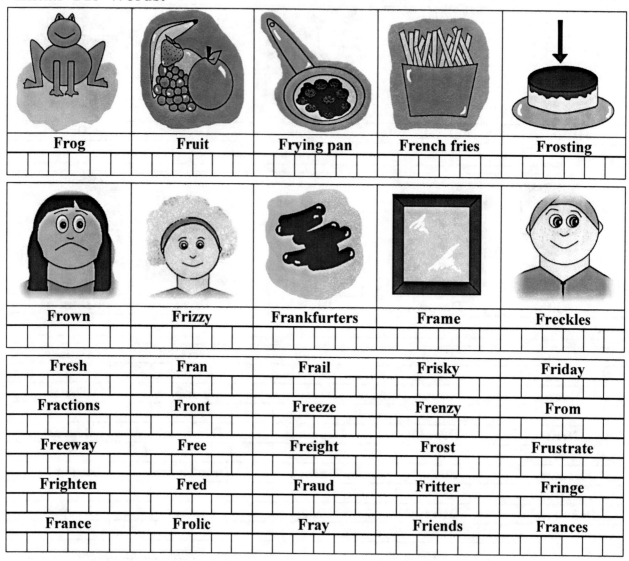

Frog	Fruit	Frying pan	French fries	Frosting

Frown	Frizzy	Frankfurters	Frame	Freckles

Fresh	Fran	Frail	Frisky	Friday
Fractions	Front	Freeze	Frenzy	From
Freeway	Free	Freight	Frost	Frustrate
Frighten	Fred	Fraud	Fritter	Fringe
France	Frolic	Fray	Friends	Frances

1. My teacher is <u>fr</u>iendly.
2. We learned about <u>fr</u>iction in science.
3. I love <u>fr</u>ied chicken.
4. My cat is very <u>fr</u>isky.
5. It is a <u>fr</u>osty morning.
6. He gave me quite a <u>fr</u>ight!
7. Her dad drives a <u>fr</u>eighter.
8. The little boy is <u>fr</u>ostbitten.
9. Tomorrow will be a <u>fr</u>igid day.
10. My daughter has the <u>fr</u>izziest hair.

Record below the dates of each Data Point (DP):
DP #1 _____ DP #2 _____ DP #3 _____ DP #4 _____ DP #5 _____ DP #6 _____

Student Name: _____ Grade: _____ Teacher/Tutor: _____

Directions: Teacher says each word or sentence aloud to student and student repeats. If student states the word incorrectly, teacher restates the word and student repeats once more. Practice on the target sound should take place at least 3 times per week for a period of no less than six weeks. Assessments should be given once a week throughout the implementation period.

Directions for giving assessments: Once a week use this sheet to asses the student's ability to pronounce the target sound. For each correct response place a '+' in the box below or adjacent to the word or sentence. For each incorrect response place a '–' in the box.

Articulation Drill Sheet
Focus Sound "GR"

Initial 'GR' Words:

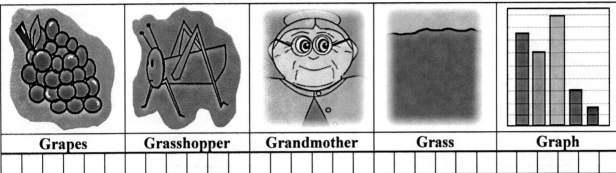

Grapes	Grasshopper	Grandmother	Grass	Graph

Grapefruit	Gravy	Graduate	Groceries	Grave

Grain	Grand	Group	Graze	Gray
Gravel	Grizzly	Gratify	Gregory	Grammar
Green	Grill	Gram	Grace	Grow
Great	Grouch	Greet	Ground	Gruff
Grew	Graceful	Grasp	Grant	Grin

1. I make good grades in school.
2. The cows are grazing on the hill.
3. My brother's name is Greg.
4. There is grease in the pan.
5. The puppy is growing.
6. The baby is grinning at me.
7. My mother will grate the cheese.
8. The grocer is my dad's best friend.
9. Grubs live in the dirt.
10. The wolf is growling.

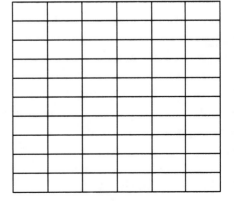

Record below the dates of each Data Point (DP):

DP #1 _____ DP #2 _____ DP #3 _____ DP #4 _____ DP #5 _____ DP #6 _____

Directions: Teacher says each word or sentence aloud to student and student repeats. If student states the word incorrectly, teacher restates the word and student repeats once more. Practice on the target sound should take place at least 3 times per week for a period of no less than six weeks. Assessments should be given once a week throughout the implementation period.

Directions for giving assessments: Once a week use this sheet to asses the student's ability to pronounce the target sound. For each correct response place a '+' in the box below or adjacent to the word or sentence. For each incorrect response place a '−' in the box.

Articulation Drill Sheet
Focus Sound "KR"

Initial 'KR/CR' Words:

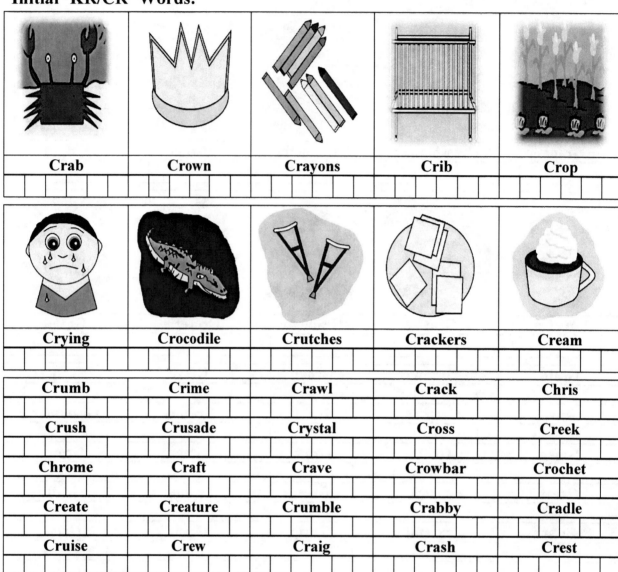

Crab	Crown	Crayons	Crib	Crop

Crying	Crocodile	Crutches	Crackers	Cream

Crumb	Crime	Crawl	Crack	Chris
Crush	Crusade	Crystal	Cross	Creek
Chrome	Craft	Crave	Crowbar	Crochet
Create	Creature	Crumble	Crabby	Cradle
Cruise	Crew	Craig	Crash	Crest

1. The baby is <u>cr</u>awling on the floor.
2. The <u>Chr</u>istmas tree has lots of lights.
3. It is <u>cr</u>owded at school.
4. My sister drives me <u>cr</u>azy!
5. I hear the <u>cr</u>icket chirping.
6. My mom cut the <u>cr</u>ust off of my sandwich.
7. I have a <u>cr</u>amp in my leg.
8. The <u>cr</u>ook stole my watch.
9. Black <u>cr</u>ows are in the tree.
10. The dishes are in the <u>cr</u>ate.

Record below the dates of each Data Point (DP):
DP #1 _____   DP #2 _____   DP #3 _____   DP #4 _____   DP #5 _____   DP #6 _____

Student Name: _____ Grade: _____ Teacher/Tutor: _____

Articulation Drill Sheet
Focus Sound "PR"

Initial 'PR' Words:

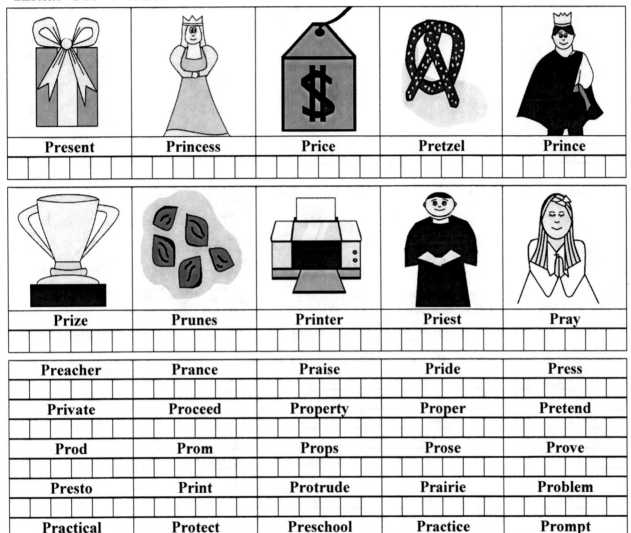

Present	Princess	Price	Pretzel	Prince

Prize	Prunes	Printer	Priest	Pray

Preacher	Prance	Praise	Pride	Press

Private	Proceed	Property	Proper	Pretend

Prod	Prom	Props	Prose	Prove

Presto	Print	Protrude	Prairie	Problem

Practical	Protect	Preschool	Practice	Prompt

1. I am making good progress!
2. My brother is working on his project.
3. My mother is very pretty.
4. I had to prove I was right.
5. My dad wants me to prosper.
6. The teacher is printing the test.
7. Primrose bushes are in the garden.
8. The prairie dog dug holes in the yard.
9. The professor taught my class.
10. I am trying to pry the lid off the jar.

Record below the dates of each Data Point (DP):
DP #1 _____ DP #2 _____ DP #3 _____ DP #4 _____ DP #5 _____ DP #6 _____

Student Name: _____ Grade: _____ Teacher/Tutor: _____

Articulation Drill Sheet
Focus Sound "TR"

Initial 'TR' Words:

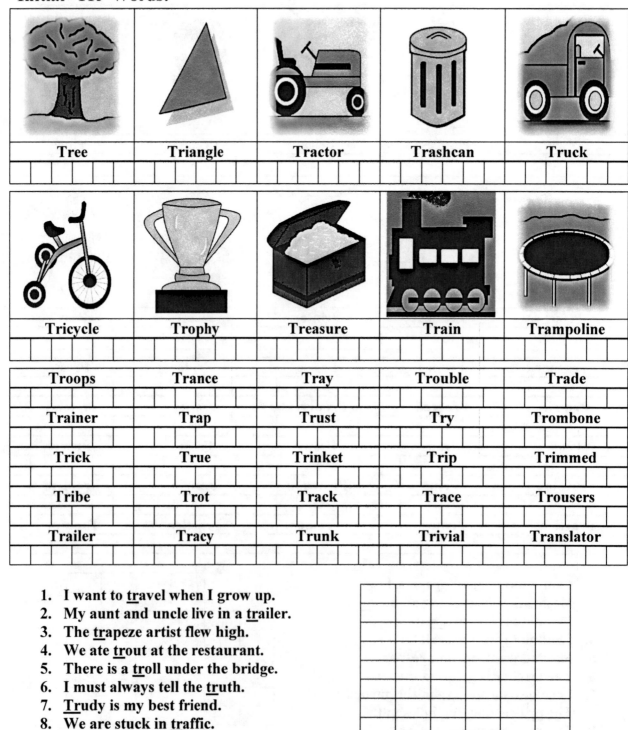

Tree	Triangle	Tractor	Trashcan	Truck

Tricycle	Trophy	Treasure	Train	Trampoline

Troops	Trance	Tray	Trouble	Trade
Trainer	Trap	Trust	Try	Trombone
Trick	True	Trinket	Trip	Trimmed
Tribe	Trot	Track	Trace	Trousers
Trailer	Tracy	Trunk	Trivial	Translator

1. I want to <u>tr</u>avel when I grow up.
2. My aunt and uncle live in a <u>tr</u>ailer.
3. The <u>tr</u>apeze artist flew high.
4. We ate <u>tr</u>out at the restaurant.
5. There is a <u>tr</u>oll under the bridge.
6. I must always tell the <u>tr</u>uth.
7. <u>Tr</u>udy is my best friend.
8. We are stuck in <u>tr</u>affic.
9. My cousin had <u>tr</u>iplets last year.
10. My family rode on the <u>tr</u>olley.

Record below the dates of each Data Point (DP):
DP #1 _____ DP #2 _____ DP #3 _____ DP #4 _____ DP #5 _____ DP #6 _____

Student Name: _____ Grade: _____ Teacher/Tutor: _____

Directions: Teacher says each word or sentence aloud to student and student repeats. If student states the word incorrectly, teacher restates the word and student repeats once more. Practice on the target sound should take place at least 3 times per week for a period of no less than six weeks. Assessments should be given once a week throughout the implementation period.

Directions for giving assessments: Once a week use this sheet to asses the student's ability to pronounce the target sound. For each correct response place a '+' in the box below or adjacent to the word or sentence. For each incorrect response place a '−' in the box.

Articulation Drill Sheet
Focus Sound "S"

Initial 'S' Words:

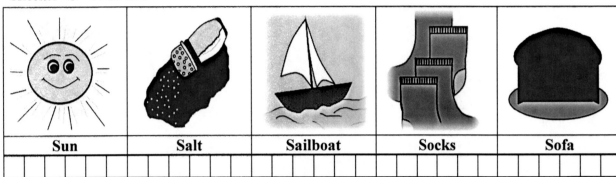

Sun	Salt	Sailboat	Socks	Sofa

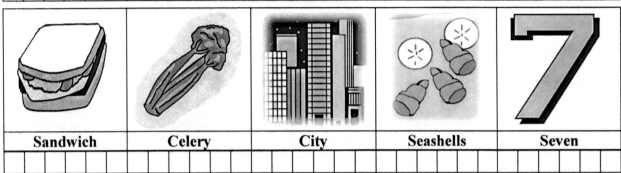

Sandwich	Celery	City	Seashells	Seven

Suit	Subtract	Cereal	Seat belt	Sandals
Safety	Surfer	Softball	Sewing	Circle
Seal	Sick	Saddle	Soup	Sign
Sailor	Sing	Seventeen	Sound	Soap
Seed	Sam	Saw	Sip	Sink

1. My grandmother <u>s</u>ent me a card.
2. I live on the left <u>s</u>ide of the street.
3. The milk has gone <u>s</u>our.
4. My bunny is <u>s</u>oft.
5. I will <u>s</u>erve mom breakfast in bed.
6. Please buy one <u>s</u>ack of potatoes.
7. My friend has <u>s</u>aved twenty dollars.
8. She <u>s</u>earched for her kitten.
9. I have a blue <u>s</u>ilk shirt.
10. Yesterday I was <u>s</u>ad.

Record below the dates of each Data Point (DP):
DP #1 _____ DP #2 _____ DP #3 _____ DP #4 _____ DP #5 _____ DP #6 _____

Student Name: _____ Grade: _____ Teacher/Tutor: _____

Articulation Drill Sheet
Focus Sound "S"

Medial 'S' Words:

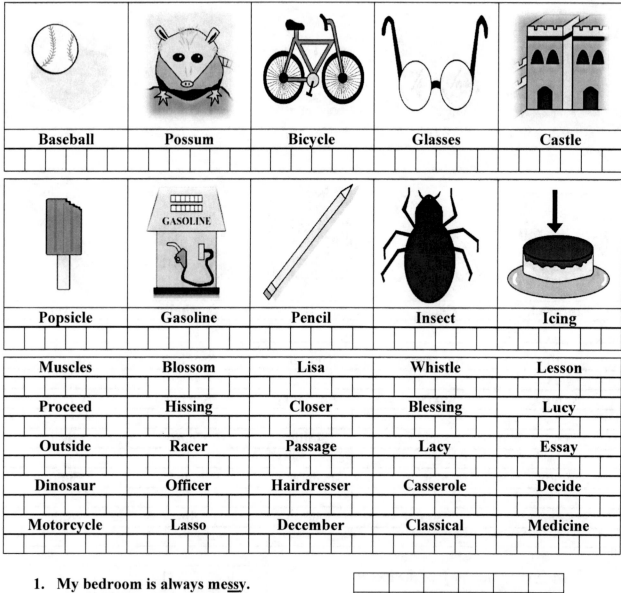

Baseball	Possum	Bicycle	Glasses	Castle

Popsicle	Gasoline	Pencil	Insect	Icing

Muscles	Blossom	Lisa	Whistle	Lesson
Proceed	Hissing	Closer	Blessing	Lucy
Outside	Racer	Passage	Lacy	Essay
Dinosaur	Officer	Hairdresser	Casserole	Decide
Motorcycle	Lasso	December	Classical	Medicine

1. My bedroom is always me<u>ss</u>y.
2. At school I li<u>s</u>ten carefully.
3. My mom has a lot of music ca<u>ss</u>ettes.
4. Her cousin is a good dan<u>c</u>er.
5. The poli<u>c</u>eman caught the thief.
6. Please leave a me<u>ss</u>age.
7. Ja<u>s</u>on is my neighbor.
8. My sister is very bo<u>ss</u>y.
9. The fu<u>ss</u>y baby finally went to sleep.
10. I can tie my shoes by my<u>s</u>elf.

Record below the dates of each Data Point (DP):
DP #1 _____ DP #2 _____ DP #3 _____ DP #4 _____ DP #5 _____ DP #6 _____

Student Name: _____ Grade: _____ Teacher/Tutor: _____

Directions: Teacher says each word or sentence aloud to student and student repeats. If student states the word incorrectly, teacher restates the word and student repeats once more. Practice on the target sound should take place at least 3 times per week for a period of no less than six weeks. Assessments should be given once a week throughout the implementation period.

Directions for giving assessments: Once a week use this sheet to asses the student's ability to pronounce the target sound. For each correct response place a '+' in the box below or adjacent to the word or sentence. For each incorrect response place a '−' in the box.

Articulation Drill Sheet
Focus Sound "S"

Final 'S' Words:

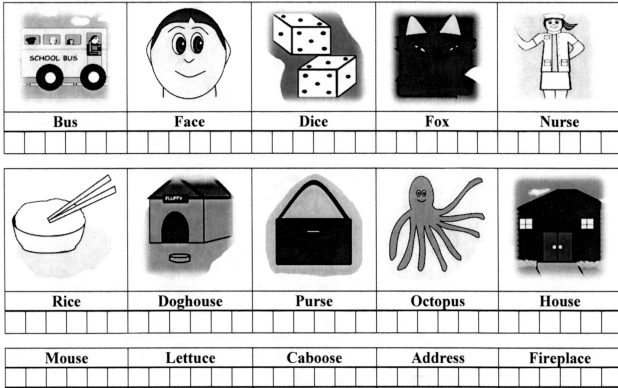

Bus	Face	Dice	Fox	Nurse

Rice	Doghouse	Purse	Octopus	House

Mouse	Lettuce	Caboose	Address	Fireplace
Mattress	Geese	Bookcase	Office	Actress
Necklace	Vase	Kiss	Fence	Hourglass
Waitress	Juice	Chase	Moose	Yes
Doris	Famous	Hippopotamus	Glorious	Rhinoceros

1. The lione<u>ss</u> protects her baby.
2. Thoma<u>s</u> is going to work.
3. My dad drinks coffee from his thermo<u>s</u>.
4. Everyone is looking for happine<u>ss</u>.
5. My teacher is very ni<u>ce</u>.
6. Tomorrow we will ride my hor<u>se</u>.
7. Thi<u>s</u> is my puppy.
8. We like to play che<u>ss</u>.
9. To<u>ss</u> me the ball.
10. I saw the movie twi<u>ce</u>.

Record below the dates of each Data Point (DP):
DP #1 _____ DP #2 _____ DP #3 _____ DP #4 _____ DP #5 _____ DP #6 _____

37

Student Name: _____ Grade: _____ Teacher/Tutor: _____

Directions: Teacher says each word or sentence aloud to student and student repeats. If student states the word incorrectly, teacher restates the word and student repeats once more. Practice on the target sound should take place at least 3 times per week for a period of no less than six weeks. Assessments should be given once a week throughout the implementation period.

Directions for giving assessments: Once a week use this sheet to asses the student's ability to pronounce the target sound. For each correct response place a '+' in the box below or adjacent to the word or sentence. For each incorrect response place a '–' in the box.

Articulation Drill Sheet
Focus Sound "SK"

Initial 'SK' Words:

Skate	Skull	Scoop	School	Skateboard

Skirt	Scarf	Skunk	Skillet	Sky

Sketchy	Scale	Scamp	Skin	Skip
Skinny	Scholar	Schedule	Scatter	Score
Skeptic	Scalpel	Scarlet	Ski	Scary
Scuba	Scalloped	Skeleton	Scuff	Scarecrow
Skimp	Skyscraper	Scorching	Scott	Scalding

1. One day I will go to Scotland.
2. I got a scooter for my birthday.
3. My dad will sketch a picture for me.
4. That boy has a scowl on his face.
5. My cousin is a good skier.
6. My sister scuffed up her shoes.
7. I have a lot of skills.
8. My class performed a skit for the school.
9. He scored three touchdowns at the game.
10. The skipper jumped out of the boat.

Record below the dates of each Data Point (DP):

DP #1 _____ DP #2 _____ DP #3 _____ DP #4 _____ DP #5 _____ DP #6 _____

Student Name: _____ Grade: _____ Teacher/Tutor: _____

Directions: Teacher says each word or sentence aloud to student and student repeats. If student states the word incorrectly, teacher restates the word and student repeats once more. Practice on the target sound should take place at least 3 times per week for a period of no less than six weeks. Assessments should be given once a week throughout the implementation period.

Directions for giving assessments: Once a week use this sheet to asses the student's ability to pronounce the target sound. For each correct response place a '+' in the box below or adjacent to the word or sentence. For each incorrect response place a '–' in the box.

Articulation Drill Sheet
Focus Sound "SL"

Initial 'SL' Words:

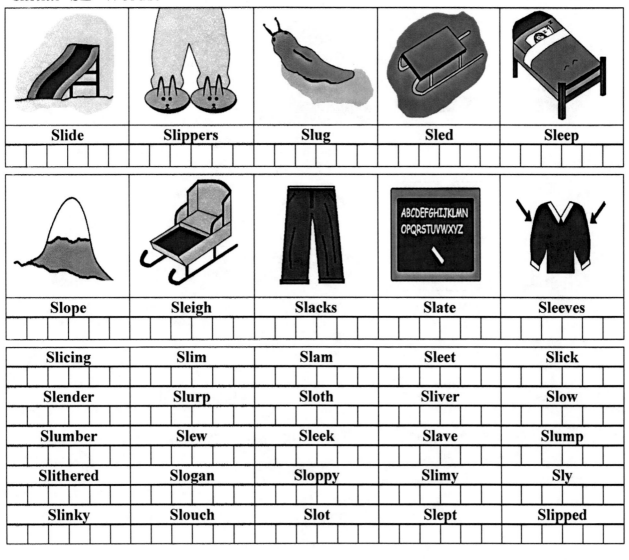

| Slide | Slippers | Slug | Sled | Sleep |

| Slope | Sleigh | Slacks | Slate | Sleeves |

Slicing	Slim	Slam	Sleet	Slick
Slender	Slurp	Sloth	Sliver	Slow
Slumber	Slew	Sleek	Slave	Slump
Slithered	Slogan	Sloppy	Slimy	Sly
Slinky	Slouch	Slot	Slept	Slipped

1. He <u>sl</u>ammed his finger in the door.
2. She fell into a pool of green <u>sl</u>ime.
3. The baby is <u>sl</u>eeping in the other room.
4. I love to eat cole <u>sl</u>aw.
5. My little brother is a <u>sl</u>owpoke.
6. She is <u>sl</u>iding down the hill.
7. He <u>sl</u>urred his words when he spoke.
8. My teacher said I wrote <u>sl</u>oppily.
9. The <u>sl</u>ats of the chair broke.
10. The pig ate the <u>sl</u>op in the bucket.

Record below the dates of each Data Point (DP):

DP #1 _____ DP #2 _____ DP #3 _____ DP #4 _____ DP #5 _____ DP #6 _____

Student Name: _____ Grade: _____ Teacher/Tutor: _____

Articulation Drill Sheet
Focus Sound "SM"

Initial 'SM' Words:

Smile	Smoke	Smart	Smell	Smaller

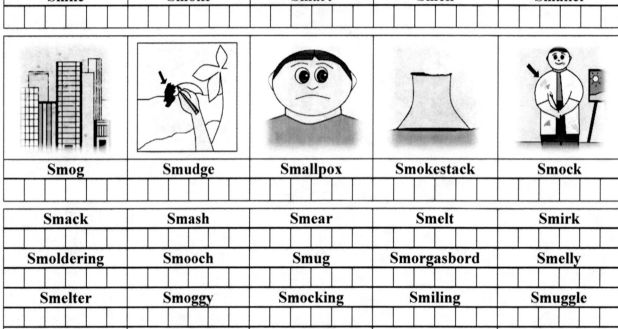

Smog	Smudge	Smallpox	Smokestack	Smock

Smack	Smash	Smear	Smelt	Smirk
Smoldering	Smooch	Smug	Smorgasbord	Smelly
Smelter	Smoggy	Smocking	Smiling	Smuggle
Smokehouse	Smother	Smooth	Smattering	Smote
Smith	Smartness	Smacked	Smirking	Smoothly

1. He is <u>sm</u>aller than me.
2. The man has a <u>sm</u>irk on his face.
3. Don't <u>sm</u>other me!
4. The <u>sm</u>ugglers stole the diamonds.
5. It is a <u>sm</u>oggy day.
6. Her lipstick is <u>sm</u>udged.
7. She is the <u>sm</u>artest student in the class.
8. My brother is <u>sm</u>acking his lips.
9. I love to eat <u>sm</u>ores when I go camping.
10. Skunks are <u>sm</u>elly animals.

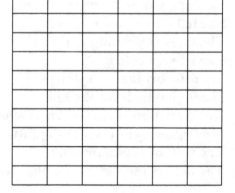

Record below the dates of each Data Point (DP):
DP #1 _____ DP #2 _____ DP #3 _____ DP #4 _____ DP #5 _____ DP #6 _____

Student Name: _____ Grade: _____ Teacher/Tutor: _____

Directions: Teacher says each word or sentence aloud to student and student repeats. If student states the word incorrectly, teacher restates the word and student repeats once more. Practice on the target sound should take place at least 3 times per week for a period of no less than six weeks. Assessments should be given once a week throughout the implementation period.

Directions for giving assessments: Once a week use this sheet to asses the student's ability to pronounce the target sound. For each correct response place a '+' in the box below or adjacent to the word or sentence. For each incorrect response place a '−' in the box.

Articulation Drill Sheet
Focus Sound "SN"

Initial 'SN' Words:

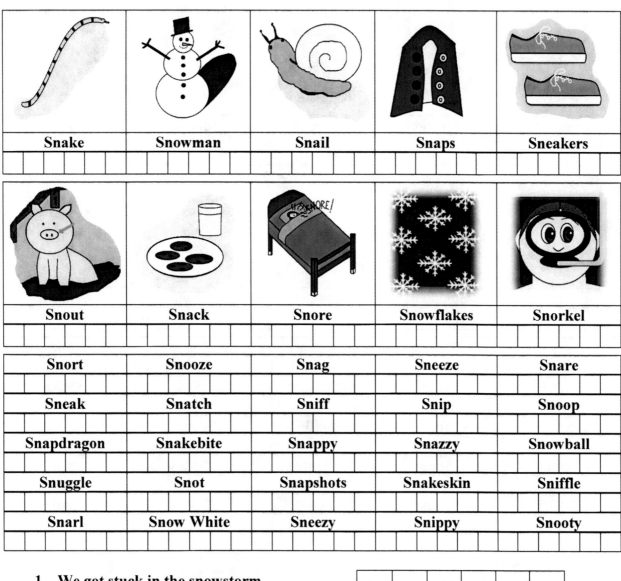

Snake	Snowman	Snail	Snaps	Sneakers

Snout	Snack	Snore	Snowflakes	Snorkel

Snort	Snooze	Snag	Sneeze	Snare
Sneak	Snatch	Sniff	Snip	Snoop
Snapdragon	Snakebite	Snappy	Snazzy	Snowball
Snuggle	Snot	Snapshots	Snakeskin	Sniffle
Snarl	Snow White	Sneezy	Snippy	Snooty

1. We got stuck in the <u>sn</u>owstorm.
2. We went <u>sn</u>orkeling in the ocean.
3. I want a <u>sn</u>owmobile for Christmas.
4. The boy <u>sn</u>ubbed his friend.
5. I always wear my <u>sn</u>ow boots outside.
6. My grandfather loves to eat red <u>sn</u>apper.
7. My little brother is <u>sn</u>eaky.
8. My family grows <u>sn</u>ap beans in the garden.
9. The <u>sn</u>owplow cleared the street.
10. My father is <u>sn</u>oring loudly.

Record below the dates of each Data Point (DP):

DP #1 _____ DP #2 _____ DP #3 _____ DP #4 _____ DP #5 _____ DP #6 _____

Student Name: _____ Grade: _____ Teacher/Tutor: _____

Directions: Teacher says each word or sentence aloud to student and student repeats. If student states the word incorrectly, teacher restates the word and student repeats once more. Practice on the target sound should take place at least 3 times per week for a period of no less than six weeks. Assessments should be given once a week throughout the implementation period.

Directions for giving assessments: Once a week use this sheet to asses the student's ability to pronounce the target sound. For each correct response place a '+' in the box below or adjacent to the word or sentence. For each incorrect response place a '–' in the box.

Articulation Drill Sheet
Focus Sound "SP"

Initial 'SP' Words:

Spider	Sponge	Spoon	Spacesuit	Spots

Sparkler	Spaghetti	Spear	Spool	Spinach

Sports car	Spooky	Spent	Spice	Spike
Speedy	Spanish	Speaker	Spy	Spoke
Spin	Split	Spilled	Spelling	Sparse
Spine	Spoil	Spite	Sport	Spud
Spotlight	Spouse	Spunk	Spout	Spade

1. I cried when I spilled my milk.
2. The cowboy has spurs on his boots.
3. There is a spider web in the corner.
4. The spacemen walked on the moon.
5. Her mother is from Spain.
6. There is a spare tire in the truck.
7. The man spoke loudly.
8. Yesterday I went to the spa.
9. The spaceship flew around the earth.
10. I am working on my speech.

Record below the dates of each Data Point (DP):
DP #1 _____ DP #2 _____ DP #3 _____ DP #4 _____ DP #5 _____ DP #6 _____

Student Name: _____ Grade: _____ Teacher/Tutor: _____

Directions: Teacher says each word or sentence aloud to student and student repeats. If student states the word incorrectly, teacher restates the word and student repeats once more. Practice on the target sound should take place at least 3 times per week for a period of no less than six weeks. Assessments should be given once a week throughout the implementation period.

Directions for giving assessments: Once a week use this sheet to asses the student's ability to pronounce the target sound. For each correct response place a '+' in the box below or adjacent to the word or sentence. For each incorrect response place a '−' in the box.

Articulation Drill Sheet
Focus Sound "ST"

Initial 'ST' Words:

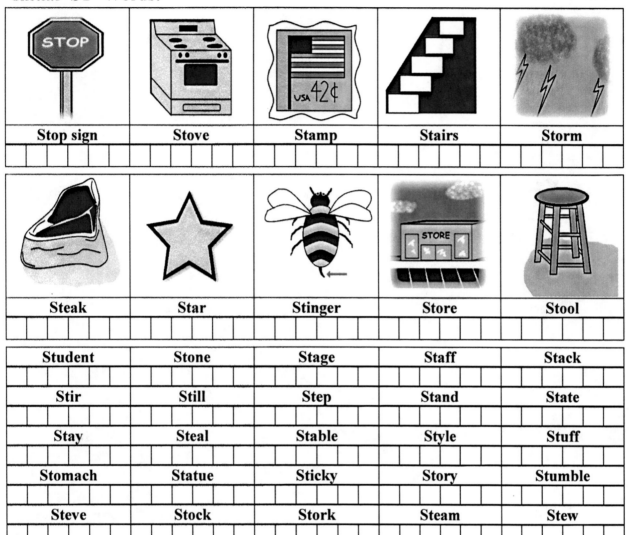

Stop sign	Stove	Stamp	Stairs	Storm

Steak	Star	Stinger	Store	Stool

Student	Stone	Stage	Staff	Stack

Stir	Still	Step	Stand	State

Stay	Steal	Stable	Style	Stuff

Stomach	Statue	Sticky	Story	Stumble

Steve	Stock	Stork	Steam	Stew

1. I found a starfish on the beach.
2. Stewart hit a home run.
3. That bread is stale.
4. My brother has six stitches in his hand.
5. Quit staring at me.
6. There are twenty students in my class.
7. I made a statement to the judge.
8. The stick bug is hard to see.
9. My mom dresses very stylish.
10. Stella is a nice girl.

Record below the dates of each Data Point (DP):

DP #1 _____ DP #2 _____ DP #3 _____ DP #4 _____ DP #5 _____ DP #6 _____

Student Name: _____ Grade: _____ Teacher/Tutor: _____

Articulation Drill Sheet
Focus Sound "SW"

Initial 'SW' Words:

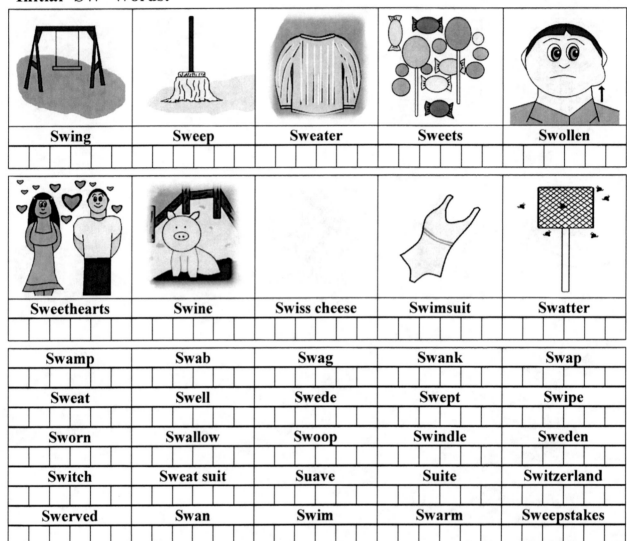

Swing	Sweep	Sweater	Sweets	Swollen

Sweethearts	Swine	Swiss cheese	Swimsuit	Swatter

Swamp	Swab	Swag	Swank	Swap
Sweat	Swell	Swede	Swept	Swipe
Sworn	Swallow	Swoop	Swindle	Sweden
Switch	Sweat suit	Suave	Suite	Switzerland
Swerved	Swan	Swim	Swarm	Sweepstakes

1. The children are <u>sw</u>inging outside.
2. I like to draw <u>sw</u>irls on my paper.
3. My mom <u>sw</u>atted away the flies.
4. The tea needs to be <u>sw</u>eetened.
5. I am <u>sw</u>eltering in this heat.
6. We walked <u>sw</u>iftly down the hall.
7. She was <u>sw</u>ept away by the flood waters.
8. They are <u>sw</u>apping baseball cards.
9. He is <u>sw</u>aying to the music.
10. The <u>sw</u>allows flew by.

Record below the dates of each Data Point (DP):
DP #1 _____ DP #2 _____ DP #3 _____ DP #4 _____ DP #5 _____ DP #6 _____

Directions: Teacher says each word or sentence aloud to student and student repeats. If student states the word incorrectly, teacher restates the word and student repeats once more. Practice on the target sound should take place at least 3 times per week for a period of no less than six weeks. Assessments should be given once a week throughout the implementation period.

Directions for giving assessments: Once a week use this sheet to asses the student's ability to pronounce the target sound. For each correct response place a '+' in the box below or adjacent to the word or sentence. For each incorrect response place a '−' in the box.

Articulation Drill Sheet
Focus Sound "Z"

Initial 'Z' Words:

Zebra	Zipper	Zoo	Zigzag	Zucchini

Zoom lens	Zeppelin	Xylophone	Zero	Zinnia

Zeus	Zip	Zoologist	Zorro	Zack
Zeal	Zone	Zap	Zen	Zany
Zing	Zelda	Zillion	Zippy	Zircon
Zulu	Zombie	Zion	Zest	Zambia
Zodiac	Zirconium	Zonal	Zealot	Zoe

1. What is your zip code?
2. He has a nice zoot suit.
3. She is zipping up the sleeping bag.
4. We are going to Zurich next week.
5. I have a plate made of zinc.
6. My aunt is studying zoology.
7. A zebu is a large animal.
8. Zachary knows how to play the guitar.
9. The zither is a musical instrument.
10. I visited the Zulu tribe in Africa.

Record below the dates of each Data Point (DP):
DP #1 _____ DP #2 _____ DP #3 _____ DP #4 _____ DP #5 _____ DP #6 _____

Articulation Drill Sheet
Focus Sound "Z"

Medial 'Z' Words:

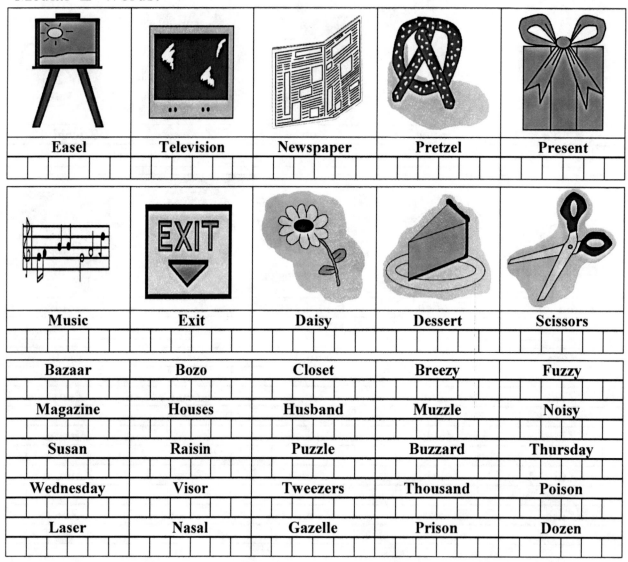

Easel	Television	Newspaper	Pretzel	Present

Music	Exit	Daisy	Dessert	Scissors

Bazaar	Bozo	Closet	Breezy	Fuzzy
Magazine	Houses	Husband	Muzzle	Noisy
Susan	Raisin	Puzzle	Buzzard	Thursday
Wednesday	Visor	Tweezers	Thousand	Poison
Laser	Nasal	Gazelle	Prison	Dozen

1. My mom is a very busy woman.
2. The wizard turned me into a frog.
3. My physician gave me medicine.
4. My sister lives in Missouri.
5. The bulldozer knocked down the wall.
6. I saw a lizard crawl up the wall.
7. Can we go to the museum?
8. I want a big piece of cheesecake.
9. Let's go sit in the gazebo.
10. Elizabeth is my middle name.

Record below the dates of each Data Point (DP):
DP #1 _____ DP #2 _____ DP #3 _____ DP #4 _____ DP #5 _____ DP #6 _____

Student Name: _____ Grade: _____ Teacher/Tutor: _____

Directions: Teacher says each word or sentence aloud to student and student repeats. If student states the word incorrectly, teacher restates the word and student repeats once more. Practice on the target sound should take place at least 3 times per week for a period of no less than six weeks. Assessments should be given once a week throughout the implementation period.

Directions for giving assessments: Once a week use this sheet to asses the student's ability to pronounce the target sound. For each correct response place a '+' in the box below or adjacent to the word or sentence. For each incorrect response place a '−' in the box.

Articulation Drill Sheet
Focus Sound "Z"

Final 'Z' Words:

Bees	Cheese	Eggs	Drums	Keys

Bananas	Babies	Nose	Apples	Rose

Animals	Kids	Knees	Lambs	Legs
Paws	Prize	Peas	Sneeze	Antlers
Cookies	Dinosaurs	Pigs	Fingers	Exercise
Flowers	Sandals	Sunrise	Sneakers	Tomatoes
Maze	Bibs	Beads	Buzzard	Ears

1. My hands are cold.
2. Her dog has fleas.
3. Do we have hotdog buns?
4. Mike broke two ribs in the accident.
5. I like to listen to jazz music.
6. My uncle has three cars.
7. My grandmother has four diamond rings.
8. The hose is in the front yard.
9. Liz is a good singer.
10. That house has four bedrooms.

Record below the dates of each Data Point (DP):

DP #1 _____ DP #2 _____ DP #3 _____ DP #4 _____ DP #5 _____ DP #6 _____

Student Name: _____ Grade: _____ Teacher/Tutor: _____

Directions: Teacher says each word or sentence aloud to student and student repeats. If student states the word incorrectly, teacher restates the word and student repeats once more. Practice on the target sound should take place at least 3 times per week for a period of no less than six weeks. Assessments should be given once a week throughout the implementation period.

Directions for giving assessments: Once a week use this sheet to asses the student's ability to pronounce the target sound. For each correct response place a '+' in the box below or adjacent to the word or sentence. For each incorrect response place a '–' in the box.

Articulation Drill Sheet
Focus Sound "L"

Initial 'L' Words:

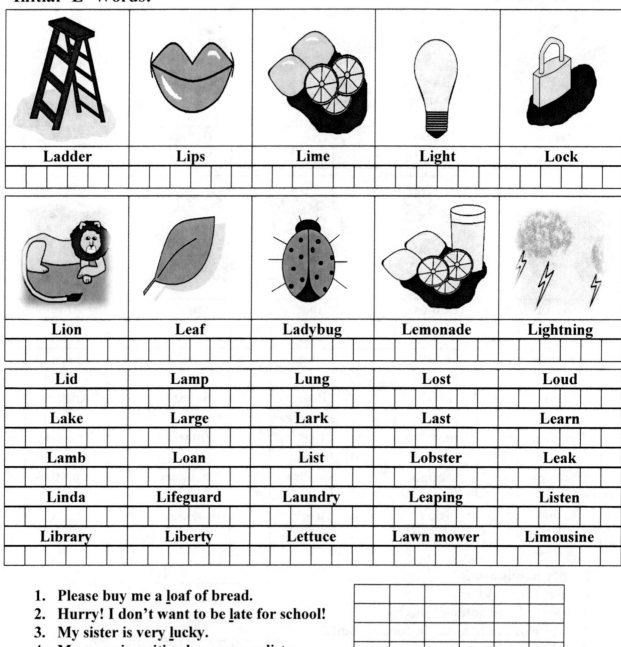

Ladder	Lips	Lime	Light	Lock

Lion	Leaf	Ladybug	Lemonade	Lightning

Lid	Lamp	Lung	Lost	Loud

| Lake | Large | Lark | Last | Learn |

| Lamb | Loan | List | Lobster | Leak |

| Linda | Lifeguard | Laundry | Leaping | Listen |

| Library | Liberty | Lettuce | Lawn mower | Limousine |

1. Please buy me a loaf of bread.
2. Hurry! I don't want to be late for school!
3. My sister is very lucky.
4. My mom is writing her grocery list.
5. Look over there!
6. Leroy is a great friend.
7. My dad always makes me laugh.
8. Did you remember to lock the door?
9. I love my cat.
10. The luggage is heavy.

Record below the dates of each Data Point (DP):
DP #1 _____ DP #2 _____ DP #3 _____ DP #4 _____ DP #5 _____ DP #6 _____

48

Directions: Teacher says each word or sentence aloud to student and student repeats. If student states the word incorrectly, teacher restates the word and student repeats once more. Practice on the target sound should take place at least 3 times per week for a period of no less than six weeks. Assessments should be given once a week throughout the implementation period.

Directions for giving assessments: Once a week use this sheet to asses the student's ability to pronounce the target sound. For each correct response place a '+' in the box below or adjacent to the word or sentence. For each incorrect response place a '–' in the box.

Articulation Drill Sheet
Focus Sound "L"

Medial 'L' Words:

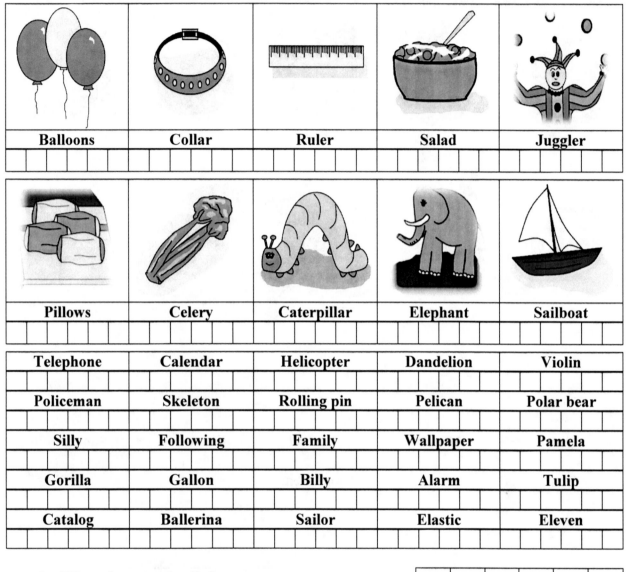

Balloons	Collar	Ruler	Salad	Juggler

Pillows	Celery	Caterpillar	Elephant	Sailboat

Telephone	Calendar	Helicopter	Dandelion	Violin
Policeman	Skeleton	Rolling pin	Pelican	Polar bear
Silly	Following	Family	Wallpaper	Pamela
Gorilla	Gallon	Billy	Alarm	Tulip
Catalog	Ballerina	Sailor	Elastic	Eleven

1. Where is my umbre**ll**a?
2. I saw an armadi**ll**o crossing the street.
3. I love orange je**ll**y beans!
4. My mom put wa**l**nuts on top of the brownies.
5. My sister got a hu**l**a hoop for her birthday.
6. That bi**ll**y goat is mean!
7. My teacher is always smi**l**ing at me.
8. Fe**l**ix broke his arm.
9. My favorite co**l**or is green.
10. I have very long eye**l**ashes.

Record below the dates of each Data Point (DP):

DP #1 _____ DP #2 _____ DP #3 _____ DP #4 _____ DP #5 _____ DP #6 _____

Directions: Teacher says each word or sentence aloud to student and student repeats. If student states the word incorrectly, teacher restates the word and student repeats once more. Practice on the target sound should take place at least 3 times per week for a period of no less than six weeks. Assessments should be given once a week throughout the implementation period.

Directions for giving assessments: Once a week use this sheet to asses the student's ability to pronounce the target sound. For each correct response place a '+' in the box below or adjacent to the word or sentence. For each incorrect response place a '–' in the box.

Articulation Drill Sheet
Focus Sound "L"

Final 'L' Words:

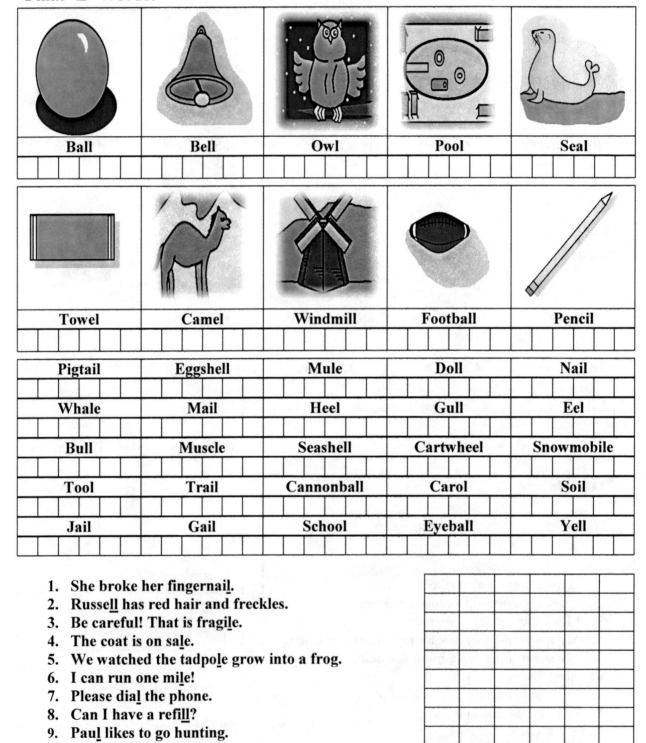

Ball	Bell	Owl	Pool	Seal

Towel	Camel	Windmill	Football	Pencil

Pigtail	Eggshell	Mule	Doll	Nail

Whale	Mail	Heel	Gull	Eel

Bull	Muscle	Seashell	Cartwheel	Snowmobile

Tool	Trail	Cannonball	Carol	Soil

Jail	Gail	School	Eyeball	Yell

1. She broke her fingernail.
2. Russell has red hair and freckles.
3. Be careful! That is fragile.
4. The coat is on sale.
5. We watched the tadpole grow into a frog.
6. I can run one mile!
7. Please dial the phone.
8. Can I have a refill?
9. Paul likes to go hunting.
10. I can't spell very well.

Record below the dates of each Data Point (DP):
DP #1 _____ DP #2 _____ DP #3 _____ DP #4 _____ DP #5 _____ DP #6 _____

Student Name: _____ Grade: _____ Teacher/Tutor: _____

Articulation Drill Sheet
Focus Sound "BL"

Initial 'BL' Words:

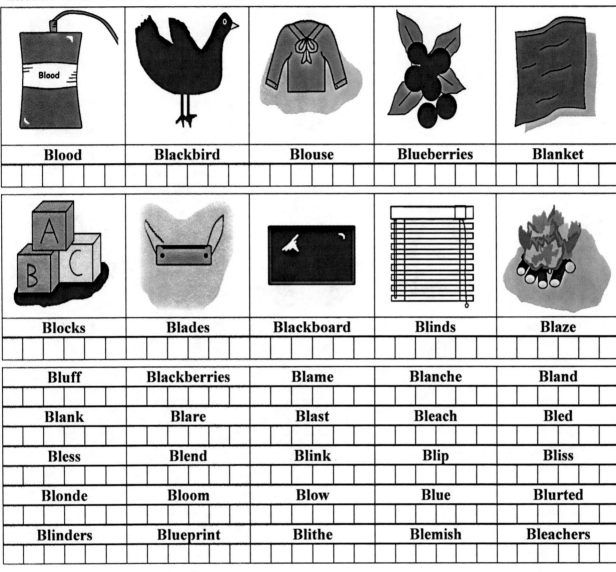

Blood	Blackbird	Blouse	Blueberries	Blanket

Blocks	Blades	Blackboard	Blinds	Blaze

Bluff	Blackberries	Blame	Blanche	Bland

Blank	Blare	Blast	Bleach	Bled

Bless	Blend	Blink	Blip	Bliss

Blonde	Bloom	Blow	Blue	Blurted

Blinders	Blueprint	Blithe	Blemish	Bleachers

1. Why is he <u>bl</u>eeding?
2. I saw an ant on a <u>bl</u>ade of grass.
3. Our car was <u>bl</u>ocked in the parking lot.
4. My mom made <u>bl</u>ueberry muffins.
5. Jane won a <u>bl</u>ue ribbon at the fair.
6. Are you <u>bl</u>uffing me?
7. His outlook is <u>bl</u>eak.
8. Why are you <u>bl</u>aming me?
9. Whales have lots of <u>bl</u>ubber.
10. My sister <u>bl</u>ots her lipstick on a tissue.

Record below the dates of each Data Point (DP):
DP #1 _____ DP #2 _____ DP #3 _____ DP #4 _____ DP #5 _____ DP #6 _____

Student Name: _____ Grade: _____ Teacher/Tutor: _____

Directions: Teacher says each word or sentence aloud to student and student repeats. If student states the word incorrectly, teacher restates the word and student repeats once more. Practice on the target sound should take place at least 3 times per week for a period of no less than six weeks. Assessments should be given once a week throughout the implementation period.

Directions for giving assessments: Once a week use this sheet to asses the student's ability to pronounce the target sound. For each correct response place a '+' in the box below or adjacent to the word or sentence. For each incorrect response place a '–' in the box.

Articulation Drill Sheet
Focus Sound "FL"

Initial 'FL' Words:

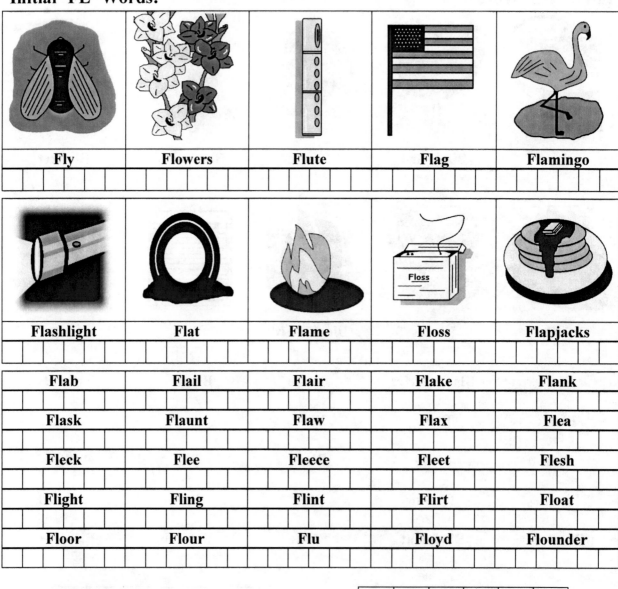

Fly	Flowers	Flute	Flag	Flamingo

Flashlight	Flat	Flame	Floss	Flapjacks

Flab	Flail	Flair	Flake	Flank
Flask	Flaunt	Flaw	Flax	Flea
Fleck	Flee	Fleece	Fleet	Flesh
Flight	Fling	Flint	Flirt	Float
Floor	Flour	Flu	Floyd	Flounder

1. My mom is a <u>fl</u>orist.
2. Our house was <u>fl</u>ooded after the storm.
3. We went to <u>Fl</u>orida over the weekend.
4. I have <u>fl</u>annel sheets on my bed.
5. We are <u>fl</u>ying to Japan tomorrow.
6. <u>Fl</u>ora is my mom's best friend.
7. My cousin saw a <u>fl</u>ock of geese.
8. He has a <u>fl</u>oppy-eared rabbit.
9. She <u>fl</u>osses her teeth every night.
10. He left in a <u>fl</u>ash.

Record below the dates of each Data Point (DP):

DP #1 _____ DP #2 _____ DP #3 _____ DP #4 _____ DP #5 _____ DP #6 _____

Student Name: _____ Grade: _____ Teacher/Tutor: _____

Directions: Teacher says each word or sentence aloud to student and student repeats. If student states the word incorrectly, teacher restates the word and student repeats once more. Practice on the target sound should take place at least 3 times per week for a period of no less than six weeks. Assessments should be given once a week throughout the implementation period.

Directions for giving assessments: Once a week use this sheet to asses the student's ability to pronounce the target sound. For each correct response place a '+' in the box below or adjacent to the word or sentence. For each incorrect response place a '−' in the box.

Articulation Drill Sheet
Focus Sound "GL"

Initial 'GL' Words:

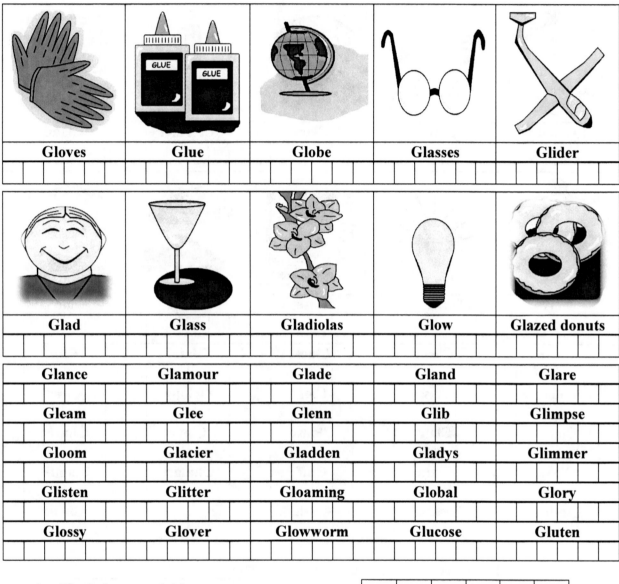

Gloves	Glue	Globe	Glasses	Glider

Glad	Glass	Gladiolas	Glow	Glazed donuts

Glance	Glamour	Glade	Gland	Glare
Gleam	Glee	Glenn	Glib	Glimpse
Gloom	Glacier	Gladden	Gladys	Glimmer
Glisten	Glitter	Gloaming	Global	Glory
Glossy	Glover	Glowworm	Glucose	Gluten

1. **Gloria** is our neighbor.
2. She seems **gloomier** than yesterday.
3. Look the words up in the **glossary**.
4. He keeps **glancing** in my direction.
5. My mom says not to be a **glutton**.
6. Today is a **glorious** day!
7. He went **gliding** down the mountain.
8. Last week we saw **Gladys**.
9. Those ladies are so **glamorous**.
10. I need a new baseball **glove**.

Record below the dates of each Data Point (DP):

DP #1 _____ DP #2 _____ DP #3 _____ DP #4 _____ DP #5 _____ DP #6 _____

Student Name: _____ Grade: _____ Teacher/Tutor: _____

Articulation Drill Sheet
Focus Sound "KL"

Initial 'KL/CL' Words:

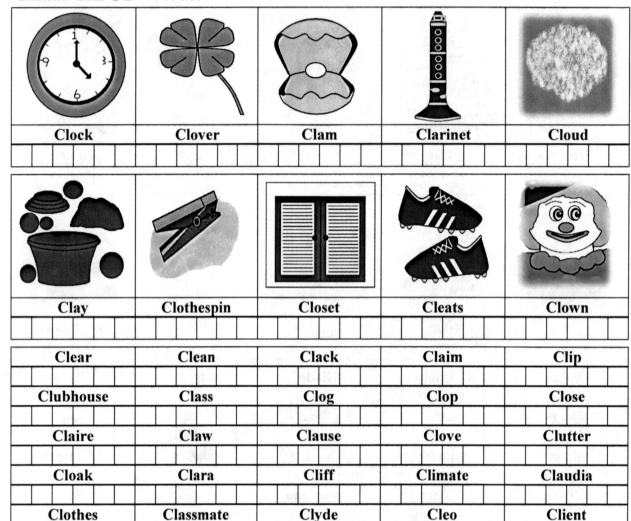

Clock	Clover	Clam	Clarinet	Cloud

Clay	Clothespin	Closet	Cleats	Clown

Clear	Clean	Clack	Claim	Clip
Clubhouse	Class	Clog	Clop	Close
Claire	Claw	Clause	Clove	Clutter
Cloak	Clara	Cliff	Climate	Claudia
Clothes	Classmate	Clyde	Cleo	Client

1. The crowd was <u>cl</u>apping at the concert.
2. We are from the same <u>cl</u>an.
3. <u>Cl</u>int is my best friend.
4. Let's go <u>cl</u>imb a tree!
5. Just <u>cl</u>ick on that button.
6. The horse's feet went "<u>cl</u>op, <u>cl</u>op."
7. I hear the bells <u>cl</u>anging.
8. Santa <u>Cl</u>aus wears a red suit.
9. <u>Cl</u>ark Kent is Superman.
10. Use the <u>cl</u>amp to hold it still.

Record below the dates of each Data Point (DP):

DP #1 _____ DP #2 _____ DP #3 _____ DP #4 _____ DP #5 _____ DP #6 _____

54

Directions: Teacher says each word or sentence aloud to student and student repeats. If student states the word incorrectly, teacher restates the word and student repeats once more. Practice on the target sound should take place at least 3 times per week for a period of no less than six weeks. Assessments should be given once a week throughout the implementation period.

Directions for giving assessments: Once a week use this sheet to asses the student's ability to pronounce the target sound. For each correct response place a '+' in the box below or adjacent to the word or sentence. For each incorrect response place a '−' in the box.

Articulation Drill Sheet
Focus Sound "PL"

Initial 'PL' Words:

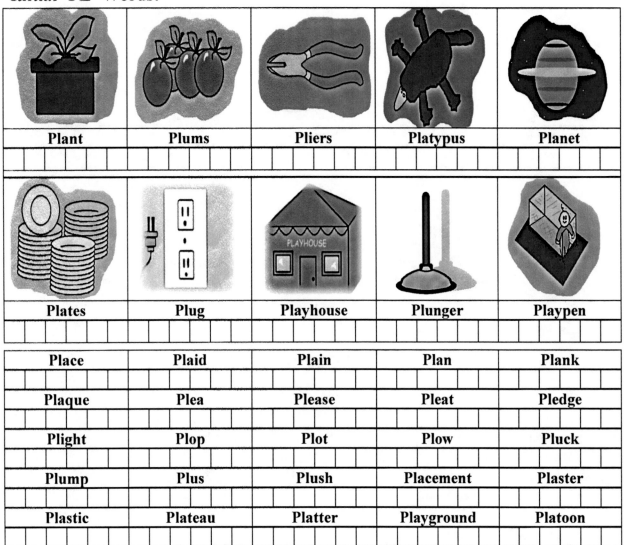

Plant	Plums	Pliers	Platypus	Planet

Plates	Plug	Playhouse	Plunger	Playpen

Place	Plaid	Plain	Plan	Plank
Plaque	Plea	Please	Pleat	Pledge
Plight	Plop	Plot	Plow	Pluck
Plump	Plus	Plush	Placement	Plaster
Plastic	Plateau	Platter	Playground	Platoon

1. What is the plural of baby?
2. Put the spoon on the place mat.
3. He stood high on the platform.
4. My dad plowed the field today.
5. One plus one equals two.
6. We flew to Hawaii in a plane.
7. The plaintiff entered the courtroom.
8. Every morning I say the pledge to the flag.
9. She is planting roses in the yard.
10. Let's go to the playroom.

Record below the dates of each Data Point (DP):
DP #1 _____ DP #2 _____ DP #3 _____ DP #4 _____ DP #5 _____ DP #6 _____

Student Name: _____ Grade: _____ Teacher/Tutor: _____

Directions: Teacher says each word or sentence aloud to student and student repeats. If student states the word incorrectly, teacher restates the word and student repeats once more. Practice on the target sound should take place at least 3 times per week for a period of no less than six weeks. Assessments should be given once a week throughout the implementation period.

Directions for giving assessments: Once a week use this sheet to asses the student's ability to pronounce the target sound. For each correct response place a '+' in the box below or adjacent to the word or sentence. For each incorrect response place a '−' in the box.

Articulation Drill Sheet
Focus Sound "SH"

Initial 'SH' Words:

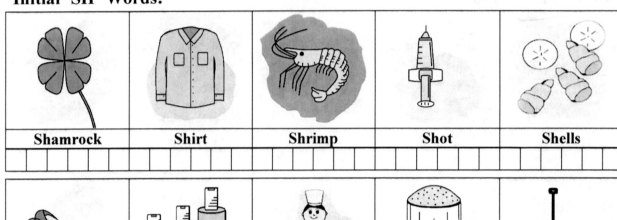

Shamrock	Shirt	Shrimp	Shot	Shells

Shoes	Shampoo	Chef	Sugar	Shovel

Shapes	Shears	Shawl	Short	Shut
Show	Shop	Shadow	Shag	Ship
Shepherd	Shaving	Share	Shoulder	Shower
Shortcake	Sherbet	Should	Shiver	Sherri
Shelter	Shatter	Sheep	Shabby	Shiny

1. He kicked me in the <u>sh</u>inbone!
2. I need new <u>sh</u>oestrings.
3. We eat <u>sh</u>ellfish when we go to the ocean.
4. Put the book on the <u>sh</u>elf.
5. <u>Sh</u>elly is my best friend.
6. The <u>sh</u>eriff caught the thief.
7. Please don't <u>sh</u>oot!
8. She needs a <u>sh</u>eet of paper.
9. The glass <u>sh</u>attered on the floor.
10. The woman was in <u>sh</u>ock.

Record below the dates of each Data Point (DP):

DP #1 _____ DP #2 _____ DP #3 _____ DP #4 _____ DP #5 _____ DP #6 _____

56

Student Name: _____ Grade: _____ Teacher/Tutor: _____

Directions: Teacher says each word or sentence aloud to student and student repeats. If student states the word incorrectly, teacher restates the word and student repeats once more. Practice on the target sound should take place at least 3 times per week for a period of no less than six weeks. Assessments should be given once a week throughout the implementation period.

Directions for giving assessments: Once a week use this sheet to asses the student's ability to pronounce the target sound. For each correct response place a '+' in the box below or adjacent to the word or sentence. For each incorrect response place a '−' in the box.

Articulation Drill Sheet
Focus Sound "SH"

Medial 'SH' Words:

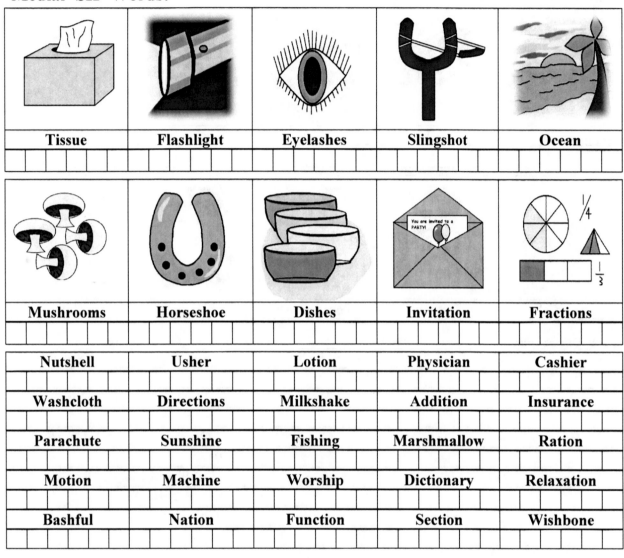

Tissue	Flashlight	Eyelashes	Slingshot	Ocean

Mushrooms	Horseshoe	Dishes	Invitation	Fractions

Nutshell	Usher	Lotion	Physician	Cashier
Washcloth	Directions	Milkshake	Addition	Insurance
Parachute	Sunshine	Fishing	Marshmallow	Ration
Motion	Machine	Worship	Dictionary	Relaxation
Bashful	Nation	Function	Section	Wishbone

1. Please pay attention.
2. Everyone is special.
3. She has a carnation on her dress.
4. We need to stop at the gas station.
5. I have to wash the dishes.
6. My dog's name is Sasha.
7. Do you know your subtraction facts?
8. There is a bug on the windshield.
9. I have a collection of toy cars.
10. I have permission to go on the fieldtrip.

Record below the dates of each Data Point (DP):
DP #1 _____ DP #2 _____ DP #3 _____ DP #4 _____ DP #5 _____ DP #6 _____

Student Name: _____ Grade: _____ Teacher/Tutor: _____

Directions: Teacher says each word or sentence aloud to student and student repeats. If student states the word incorrectly, teacher restates the word and student repeats once more. Practice on the target sound should take place at least 3 times per week for a period of no less than six weeks. Assessments should be given once a week throughout the implementation period.

Directions for giving assessments: Once a week use this sheet to asses the student's ability to pronounce the target sound. For each correct response place a '+' in the box below or adjacent to the word or sentence. For each incorrect response place a '–' in the box.

Articulation Drill Sheet
Focus Sound "SH"

Final 'SH' Words:

Fish	Cash	Dish	Brush	Leash

Starfish	Radish	Toothbrush	Hush	Push

Josh	Dash	Hash	Swish	Stash
Wash	Rash	Nash	Mash	Flush
Brash	Ash	Clash	Crash	Crush
Relish	Ticklish	Mustache	Publish	English
Ambush	Finish	Irish	Childish	Varnish

1. There is a pink sash on my dress.
2. The snow has turned to slush.
3. I have a blemish on my face.
4. Mario speaks Spanish.
5. She caught crayfish in the creek.
6. Go feed the goldfish.
7. He is acting foolish.
8. My mom will punish me.
9. Take the car to the car wash.
10. Dad will take out the trash.

Record below the dates of each Data Point (DP):
DP #1 _____ DP #2 _____ DP #3 _____ DP #4 _____ DP #5 _____ DP #6 _____

Student Name: _____ Grade: _____ Teacher/Tutor: _____

<u>Directions</u>: Teacher says each word or sentence aloud to student and student repeats. If student states the word incorrectly, teacher restates the word and student repeats once more. Practice on the target sound should take place at least 3 times per week for a period of no less than six weeks. Assessments should be given once a week throughout the implementation period.

<u>Directions for giving assessments</u>: Once a week use this sheet to asses the student's ability to pronounce the target sound. For each correct response place a '+' in the box below or adjacent to the word or sentence. For each incorrect response place a '–' in the box.

Articulation Drill Sheet
Focus Sound "CH"

Initial 'CH' Words:

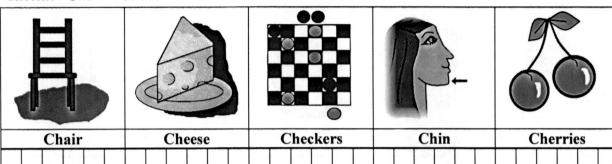

Chair	Cheese	Checkers	Chin	Cherries

Chimney	Chopsticks	Cheetah	Chocolate	Charge cards

Choke	Chad	Chain	Chalk	Champ
Change	Charles	Churn	Chart	Chat
Cheap	Cheat	Chill	Chum	Chew
Chow	Chimp	Cheerleaders	Chubby	Chinese
Chick	Churning	Children	Challenge	Chipmunk

1. I finished reading <u>ch</u>apter four.
2. Let's take a <u>ch</u>ance.
3. Do you know how to play <u>ch</u>ess?
4. I <u>ch</u>ipped my tooth.
5. My sister has the <u>ch</u>ickenpox.
6. I hear birds <u>ch</u>irping.
7. My teacher is a <u>ch</u>eerful person.
8. Have you finished your <u>ch</u>ores?
9. My mom has a <u>ch</u>arm bracelet.
10. Have you ever been to <u>Ch</u>ina?

Record below the dates of each Data Point (DP):

DP #1 _____   DP #2 _____   DP #3 _____   DP #4 _____   DP #5 _____   DP #6 _____

Student Name: _____ Grade: _____ Teacher/Tutor: _____

Directions: Teacher says each word or sentence aloud to student and student repeats. If student states the word incorrectly, teacher restates the word and student repeats once more. Practice on the target sound should take place at least 3 times per week for a period of no less than six weeks. Assessments should be given once a week throughout the implementation period.

Directions for giving assessments: Once a week use this sheet to asses the student's ability to pronounce the target sound. For each correct response place a '+' in the box below or adjacent to the word or sentence. For each incorrect response place a '–' in the box.

Articulation Drill Sheet
Focus Sound "CH"

Medial 'CH' Words:

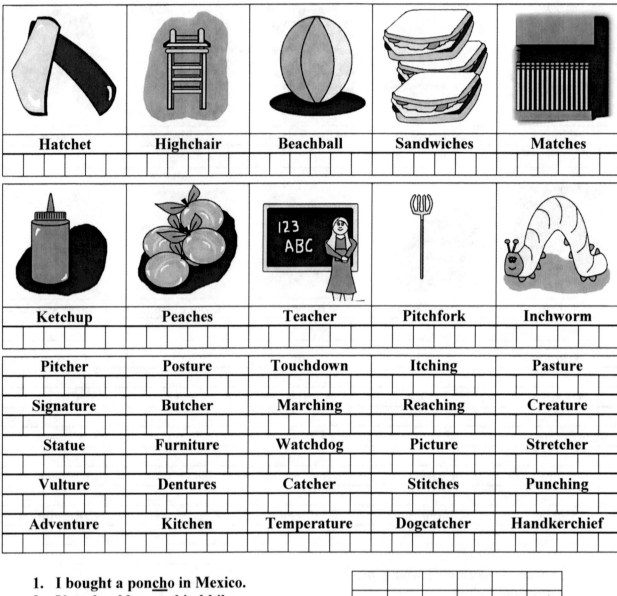

Hatchet	Highchair	Beachball	Sandwiches	Matches

Ketchup	Peaches	Teacher	Pitchfork	Inchworm

Pitcher	Posture	Touchdown	Itching	Pasture
Signature	Butcher	Marching	Reaching	Creature
Statue	Furniture	Watchdog	Picture	Stretcher
Vulture	Dentures	Catcher	Stitches	Punching
Adventure	Kitchen	Temperature	Dogcatcher	Handkerchief

1. I bought a poncho in Mexico.
2. You should never hitchhike.
3. Do you have any questions?
4. Richard is a good artist.
5. That boy is full of mischief.
6. Where is Mitchell?
7. The rancher has many horses.
8. The light fixture is beautiful.
9. Go sit on the bleachers.
10. She must use crutches to walk.

Record below the dates of each Data Point (DP):
DP #1 _____ DP #2 _____ DP #3 _____ DP #4 _____ DP #5 _____ DP #6 _____

Directions: Teacher says each word or sentence aloud to student and student repeats. If student states the word incorrectly, teacher restates the word and student repeats once more. Practice on the target sound should take place at least 3 times per week for a period of no less than six weeks. Assessments should be given once a week throughout the implementation period.

Directions for giving assessments: Once a week use this sheet to asses the student's ability to pronounce the target sound. For each correct response place a '+' in the box below or adjacent to the word or sentence. For each incorrect response place a '−' in the box.

Articulation Drill Sheet
Focus Sound "CH"

Final 'CH' Words:

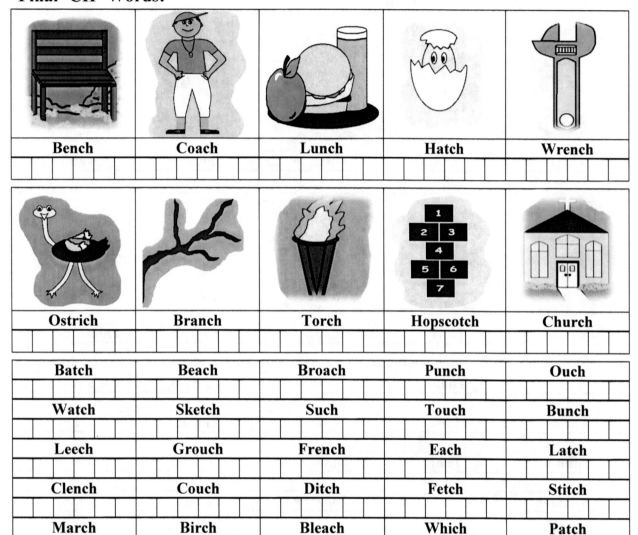

Bench	Coach	Lunch	Hatch	Wrench

Ostrich	Branch	Torch	Hopscotch	Church

Batch	Beach	Broach	Punch	Ouch

Watch	Sketch	Such	Touch	Bunch

Leech	Grouch	French	Each	Latch

Clench	Couch	Ditch	Fetch	Stitch

March	Birch	Bleach	Which	Patch

1. The bird sat on his per<u>ch</u>.
2. I love to mun<u>ch</u> on popcorn.
3. I stret<u>ch</u> when I first get up in the morning.
4. Popeye eats spina<u>ch</u>.
5. Please flip down the swit<u>ch</u>.
6. Mit<u>ch</u> is coming home today.
7. She gave a great spee<u>ch</u>.
8. The Joey is in his mother's pou<u>ch</u>.
9. A roa<u>ch</u> crawled on the table.
10. Please go unlat<u>ch</u> the door.

Record below the dates of each Data Point (DP):

DP #1 _____ DP #2 _____ DP #3 _____ DP #4 _____ DP #5 _____ DP #6 _____

Student Name: _____ Grade: _____ Teacher/Tutor: _____

Directions: Teacher says each word or sentence aloud to student and student repeats. If student states the word incorrectly, teacher restates the word and student repeats once more. Practice on the target sound should take place at least 3 times per week for a period of no less than six weeks. Assessments should be given once a week throughout the implementation period.

Directions for giving assessments: Once a week use this sheet to asses the student's ability to pronounce the target sound. For each correct response place a '+' in the box below or adjacent to the word or sentence. For each incorrect response place a '–' in the box.

Articulation Drill Sheet
Focus Sound "TH" (Voiceless)

Initial 'TH' Words (Voiceless):

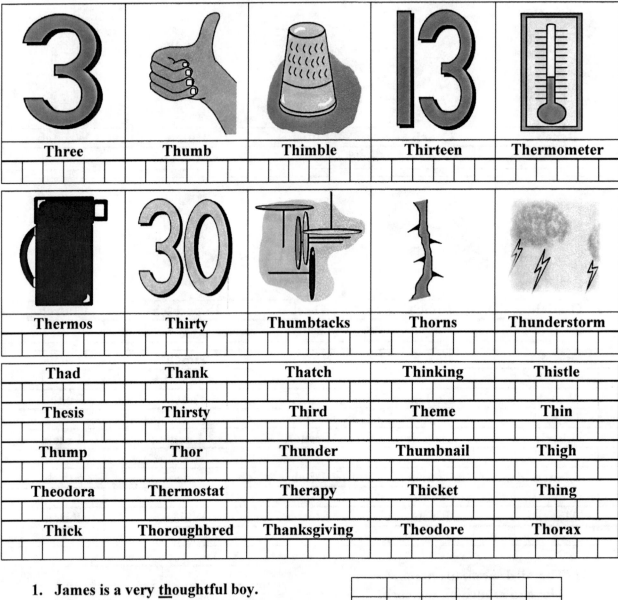

Three	Thumb	Thimble	Thirteen	Thermometer

Thermos	Thirty	Thumbtacks	Thorns	Thunderstorm

Thad	Thank	Thatch	Thinking	Thistle
Thesis	Thirsty	Third	Theme	Thin
Thump	Thor	Thunder	Thumbnail	Thigh
Theodora	Thermostat	Therapy	Thicket	Thing
Thick	Thoroughbred	Thanksgiving	Theodore	Thorax

1. James is a very <u>th</u>oughtful boy.
2. My mom turned <u>th</u>irty-seven on Sunday.
3. Last week we saw a play at the <u>th</u>eater.
4. The stove costs one <u>th</u>ousand dollars.
5. We'll go on a field trip next <u>Th</u>ursday.
6. I am <u>th</u>ankful for my parents.
7. What color <u>th</u>read do you need?
8. She is <u>th</u>inner than me.
9. We'll go on vacation in <u>th</u>irty-one days!
10. Amy broke her <u>th</u>ighbone.

Record below the dates of each Data Point (DP):
DP #1 _____ DP #2 _____ DP #3 _____ DP #4 _____ DP #5 _____ DP #6 _____

Directions: Teacher says each word or sentence aloud to student and student repeats. If student states the word incorrectly, teacher restates the word and student repeats once more. Practice on the target sound should take place at least 3 times per week for a period of no less than six weeks. Assessments should be given once a week throughout the implementation period.

Directions for giving assessments: Once a week use this sheet to asses the student's ability to pronounce the target sound. For each correct response place a '+' in the box below or adjacent to the word or sentence. For each incorrect response place a '–' in the box.

Articulation Drill Sheet
Focus Sound "TH" (Voiced)

Initial 'TH' Words (Voiced):

This	That	There	Thyself	Theirs

These	Those	Them	Themselves	They

Than	The	Their	Then	Thence
They'd	They'll	They're	They've	Thine
Thou	Though	Thus	Thy	Thereby
Therein	Thereof	Thereon	Therewith	Therefore
Thereabouts	Thereunder	Thereupon	Thereto	Thereafter

1. <u>Th</u>ey need to be more careful.
2. <u>Th</u>ey've got four cars.
3. Honor <u>th</u>y mother and father.
4. She went to <u>th</u>e store.
5. I am bigger <u>th</u>an you.
6. I am a friend of <u>th</u>ine.
7. <u>Th</u>ey'll be sorry tomorrow.
8. He hit the car and <u>th</u>en he hit his head.
9. Oh how I love <u>th</u>ee.
10. It was our fault <u>th</u>us we had to pay.

Record below the dates of each Data Point (DP):

DP #1 _____ DP #2 _____ DP #3 _____ DP #4 _____ DP #5 _____ DP #6 _____

Student Name: _____ Grade: _____ Teacher/Tutor: _____

Articulation Drill Sheet
Focus Sound "TH" (Voiceless)

Medial 'TH' Words (Voiceless):

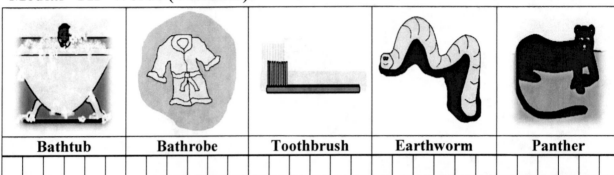

Bathtub	Bathrobe	Toothbrush	Earthworm	Panther

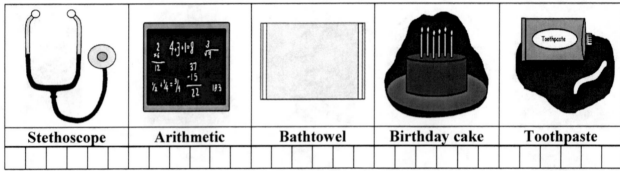

Stethoscope	Arithmetic	Bathowel	Birthday cake	Toothpaste

Author	Athlete	Breathless	Ethan	Healthy
Kathy	Method	Mothball	Nothing	Pathway
Something	Southeast	Toothpick	Truthful	Wealthy
Worthwhile	Youthful	Anything	Apathy	Dorothy
Marathon	Timothy	Ruthless	Timothy	Tooth fairy

1. Katherine has two horses.
2. He participated in a triathlon.
3. Did you get everything?
4. My dad has a toothache.
5. The python slid up the tree.
6. Pick up your playthings.
7. The rosethorns cut my finger.
8. She has a youthful face.
9. Nathan hit me!
10. My brother is in the fifth-grade.

Record below the dates of each Data Point (DP):
DP #1 _____   DP #2 _____   DP #3 _____   DP #4 _____   DP #5 _____   DP #6 _____

Student Name: _____ Grade: _____ Teacher/Tutor: _____

Articulation Drill Sheet
Focus Sound "TH" (Voiced)

Medial 'TH' Words (Voiced):

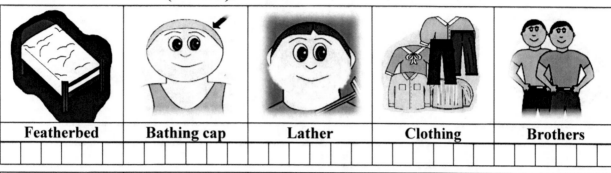

Featherbed	Bathing cap	Lather	Clothing	Brothers

Bathing suits	Grandmother	Grandfather	Feathers	Bathing

Although	Neither	Fatherhood	Worthy	Without
Soothing	Within	Fair-weather	Heather	Fathom
Teething	Southern	Breather	Stepfather	Stepmother
Withdrawing	Weatherman	Smoothest	Brotherly	Leather
Altogether	Zither	Withstand	Gathering	Breathing

1. My mom is the best mother in the world.
2. My sister is bothering me.
3. I would rather go with you.
4. How is the weather in Hawaii?
5. Jimmy is my brother-in-law.
6. She went sunbathing at the beach.
7. That boy has rhythm.
8. Where is your father?
9. The other day I was sick.
10. You can either go or stay home.

Record below the dates of each Data Point (DP):

DP #1 _____ DP #2 _____ DP #3 _____ DP #4 _____ DP #5 _____ DP #6 _____

Student Name: _____ Grade: _____ Teacher/Tutor: _____

Directions: Teacher says each word or sentence aloud to student and student repeats. If student states the word incorrectly, teacher restates the word and student repeats once more. Practice on the target sound should take place at least 3 times per week for a period of no less than six weeks. Assessments should be given once a week throughout the implementation period.

Directions for giving assessments: Once a week use this sheet to asses the student's ability to pronounce the target sound. For each correct response place a '+' in the box below or adjacent to the word or sentence. For each incorrect response place a '–' in the box.

Articulation Drill Sheet
Focus Sound "TH" (Voiceless)

Final 'TH' Words (Voiceless):

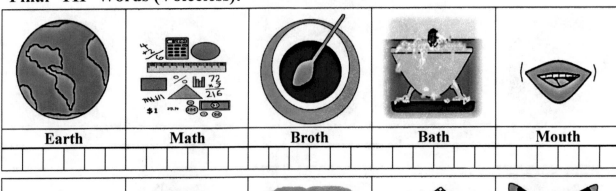

Earth	Math	Broth	Bath	Mouth

Teeth	Wreath	Tooth	Tablecloth	Moth

Cloth	Fifth	Mirth	Booth	Sloth

Birdbath	Youth	Beneath	Dishcloth	Cottonmouth

Locksmith	Mammoth	North	Path	Strength

Month	South	Length	Warmth	Keith

Depth	Beth	Oath	Froth	Blacksmith

1. My dad works as a goldsmi<u>th</u>.
2. Her fai<u>th</u> is strong.
3. Kenne<u>th</u> is the fastest boy in my class.
4. The key is undernea<u>th</u> the mat.
5. He just had a grow<u>th</u> spurt.
6. Last night I had a bubble ba<u>th</u>.
7. Queen Elizabe<u>th</u> dropped her crown.
8. Have you read the book Macbe<u>th</u>?
9. I have lost all of my baby tee<u>th</u>.
10. That man has bad brea<u>th</u>.

Record below the dates of each Data Point (DP):
DP #1 _____ DP #2 _____ DP #3 _____ DP #4 _____ DP #5 _____ DP #6 _____

Student Name: _____ Grade: _____ Teacher/Tutor: _____

Articulation Drill Sheet
Focus Sound "F"

Initial 'F' Words:

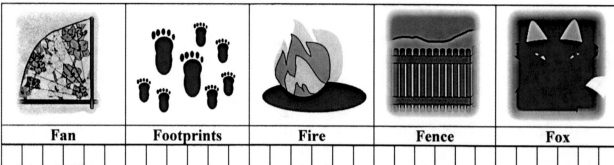

Fan	Footprints	Fire	Fence	Fox

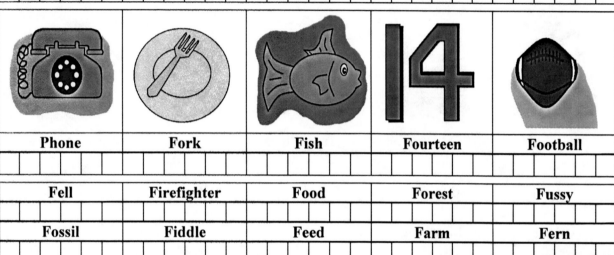

Phone	Fork	Fish	Fourteen	Football

Fell	Firefighter	Food	Forest	Fussy
Fossil	Fiddle	Feed	Farm	Fern
Fawn	Film	Face	Fingers	Fudge
Final	Falcon	Famous	Fable	Fellow
Forward	Fairy	Forget	Photo	Father

1. Today is my sister's <u>f</u>ourth birthday.
2. I am <u>f</u>irst in line.
3. Please <u>f</u>orgive me.
4. Can you help me <u>f</u>ind my keys?
5. There is a <u>f</u>ull moon tonight.
6. I have to <u>f</u>old the towels.
7. My cat is very <u>f</u>urry.
8. She is <u>f</u>iling the papers.
9. Please <u>f</u>ix my bike.
10. My mom is a <u>f</u>emale.

Record below the dates of each Data Point (DP):

DP #1 _____ DP #2 _____ DP #3 _____ DP #4 _____ DP #5 _____ DP #6 _____

Student Name: _____ Grade: _____ Teacher/Tutor: _____

Directions: Teacher says each word or sentence aloud to student and student repeats. If student states the word incorrectly, teacher restates the word and student repeats once more. Practice on the target sound should take place at least 3 times per week for a period of no less than six weeks. Assessments should be given once a week throughout the implementation period.

Directions for giving assessments: Once a week use this sheet to asses the student's ability to pronounce the target sound. For each correct response place a '+' in the box below or adjacent to the word or sentence. For each incorrect response place a '–' in the box.

Articulation Drill Sheet
Focus Sound "F"

Medial 'F' Words:

Waffle	Coffee	Golfball	Daffodil	Alphabet

Elephant	Muffin	Dolphin	Sofa	Campfire

Trophy	Barefoot	Before	Bonfire	Cupful
Infant	Laughing	Leafy	Often	Outfield
Lifeguard	Unfold	Profile	Gopher	Taffy
Transfer	Golfer	Handful	Confuse	Crayfish
Rainfall	Useful	Office	Catfish	Hayfork

1. Let's go eat break**f**ast.
2. I am thank**f**ul for my food.
3. We are stuck in tra**ff**ic.
4. He plays in the out**f**ield.
5. She has a pocket**f**ul of marbles.
6. So**ph**ie is a good girl.
7. Last night we ate le**f**tovers.
8. Let's go where the bu**ff**alo roam!
9. My kitten is very play**f**ul.
10. Cli**ff**ord is a big red dog.

Record below the dates of each Data Point (DP):
DP #1 _____ DP #2 _____ DP #3 _____ DP #4 _____ DP #5 _____ DP #6 _____

Student Name: _____ Grade: _____ Teacher/Tutor: _____

Directions: Teacher says each word or sentence aloud to student and student repeats. If student states the word incorrectly, teacher restates the word and student repeats once more. Practice on the target sound should take place at least 3 times per week for a period of no less than six weeks. Assessments should be given once a week throughout the implementation period.
Directions for giving assessments: Once a week use this sheet to asses the student's ability to pronounce the target sound. For each correct response place a '+' in the box below or adjacent to the word or sentence. For each incorrect response place a '–' in the box.

Articulation Drill Sheet
Focus Sound "F"

Final 'F' Words:

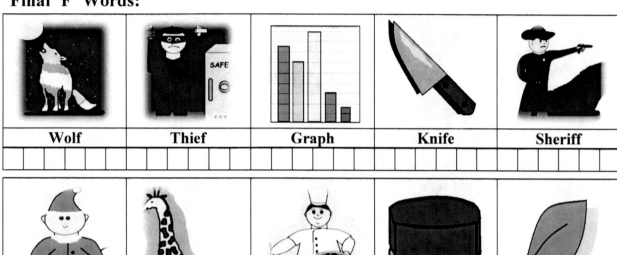

Wolf	Thief	Graph	Knife	Sheriff

Elf	Giraffe	Chef	Loaf	Leaf

Laugh	Chief	Cough	Cuff	Roof

Hoof	Safe	Off	Beef	Calf

Jeff	Cliff	Rough	Staff	Tough

Puff	Belief	Joseph	Huff	Reef

Autograph	Handkerchief	Photograph	Housewife	Paragraph

1. He is such a show-off.
2. That is enough!
3. Tammy is my brother's wife.
4. What proof do you have?
5. Sniff the rose.
6. Please be brief.
7. I love my life.
8. My mom is a housewife.
9. My watch is waterproof.
10. The dog said, "Woof, Woof."

Record below the dates of each Data Point (DP):
DP #1 _____ DP #2 _____ DP #3 _____ DP #4 _____ DP #5 _____ DP #6 _____

Student Name: _____ Grade: _____ Teacher/Tutor: _____

Articulation Drill Sheet
Focus Sound "V"

Initial 'V' Words:

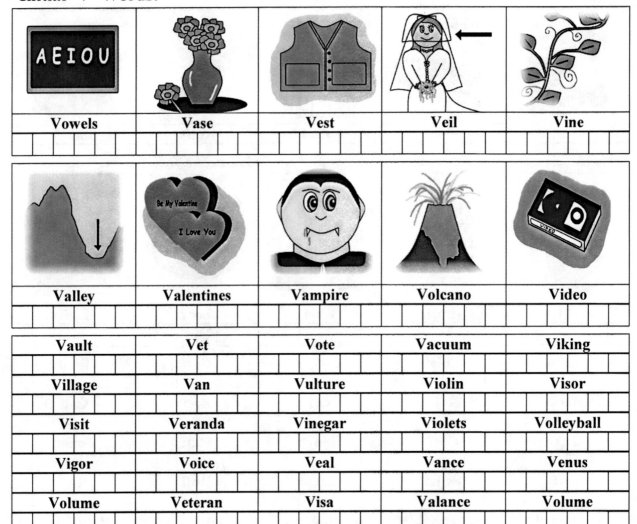

Vowels	Vase	Vest	Veil	Vine

Valley	Valentines	Vampire	Volcano	Video

Vault	Vet	Vote	Vacuum	Viking
Village	Van	Vulture	Violin	Visor
Visit	Veranda	Vinegar	Violets	Volleyball
Vigor	Voice	Veal	Vance	Venus
Volume	Veteran	Visa	Valance	Volume

1. She has a beautiful voice.
2. Vicky is my best friend.
3. Watch out for that viper!
4. What is the value of that car?
5. He wants to marry Vera.
6. We're moving to Vermont.
7. I love vanilla ice cream.
8. Which vehicle will we take?
9. She vowed to love her husband.
10. I love lots of vegetables in my salad.

Record below the dates of each Data Point (DP):
DP #1 _____ DP #2 _____ DP #3 _____ DP #4 _____ DP #5 _____ DP #6 _____

Student Name: _____ Grade: _____ Teacher/Tutor: _____

Directions: Teacher says each word or sentence aloud to student and student repeats. If student states the word incorrectly, teacher restates the word and student repeats once more. Practice on the target sound should take place at least 3 times per week for a period of no less than six weeks. Assessments should be given once a week throughout the implementation period.

Directions for giving assessments: Once a week use this sheet to asses the student's ability to pronounce the target sound. For each correct response place a '+' in the box below or adjacent to the word or sentence. For each incorrect response place a '–' in the box.

Articulation Drill Sheet
Focus Sound "V"

Medial 'V' Words:

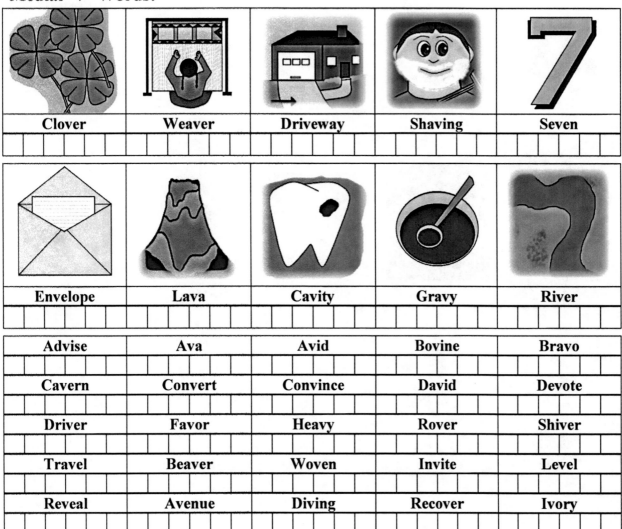

Clover	Weaver	Driveway	Shaving	Seven

Envelope	Lava	Cavity	Gravy	River

Advise	Ava	Avid	Bovine	Bravo
Cavern	Convert	Convince	David	Devote
Driver	Favor	Heavy	Rover	Shiver
Travel	Beaver	Woven	Invite	Level
Reveal	Avenue	Diving	Recover	Ivory

1. My dad has a Che**v**y truck.
2. He has a high fe**v**er.
3. We went skiing in Den**v**er.
4. What is your fa**v**orite color?
5. I have a lo**v**ing family.
6. I have se**v**eral books.
7. Let's go to the carni**v**al!
8. He is the go**v**ernor of our state.
9. I'll celebrate Thanksgi**v**ing in Maine.
10. Le**v**i is a friend of mine.

Record below the dates of each Data Point (DP):
DP #1 _____ DP #2 _____ DP #3 _____ DP #4 _____ DP #5 _____ DP #6 _____

Student Name: _____ Grade: _____ Teacher/Tutor: _____

Directions: Teacher says each word or sentence aloud to student and student repeats. If student states the word incorrectly, teacher restates the word and student repeats once more. Practice on the target sound should take place at least 3 times per week for a period of no less than six weeks. Assessments should be given once a week throughout the implementation period.

Directions for giving assessments: Once a week use this sheet to asses the student's ability to pronounce the target sound. For each correct response place a '+' in the box below or adjacent to the word or sentence. For each incorrect response place a '–' in the box.

Articulation Drill Sheet
Focus Sound "V"

Final 'V' Words:

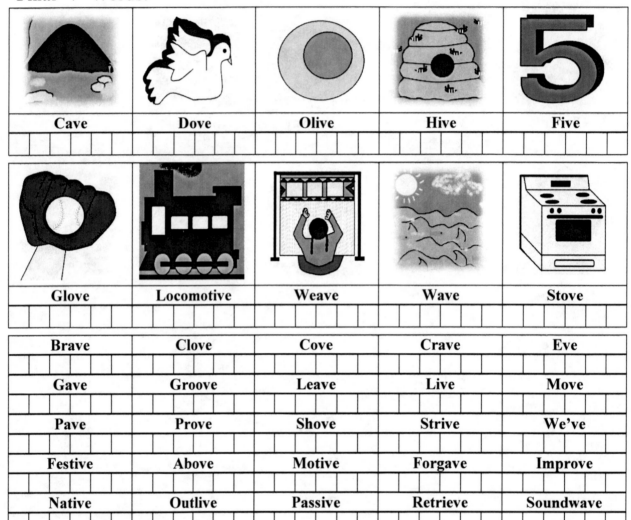

Cave	Dove	Olive	Hive	Five

Glove	Locomotive	Weave	Wave	Stove

Brave	Clove	Cove	Crave	Eve
Gave	Groove	Leave	Live	Move
Pave	Prove	Shove	Strive	We've
Festive	Above	Motive	Forgave	Improve
Native	Outlive	Passive	Retrieve	Soundwave

1. You've got beautiful hair.
2. Did you save some for me?
3. Please remove your hat.
4. Are you scared to skydive?
5. We will survive.
6. Give me your hand
7. You must behave yourself!
8. I will always love you.
9. You've always got a friend in me.
10. I am not a slave.

Record below the dates of each Data Point (DP):
DP #1 _____ DP #2 _____ DP #3 _____ DP #4 _____ DP #5 _____ DP #6 _____

72

Directions: Teacher says each word or sentence aloud to student and student repeats. If student states the word incorrectly, teacher restates the word and student repeats once more. Practice on the target sound should take place at least 3 times per week for a period of no less than six weeks. Assessments should be given once a week throughout the implementation period.

Directions for giving assessments: Once a week use this sheet to asses the student's ability to pronounce the target sound. For each correct response place a '+' in the box below or adjacent to the word or sentence. For each incorrect response place a '−' in the box.

Articulation Drill Sheet
Focus Sound "K/C"

Initial 'K/C' Words:

Key	Cat	Carrot	Caterpillar	King

Kite	Computer	Kangaroo	Corn	Comb

Car	Kids	Candy	Cowgirl	Cow
Coach	Kitchen	Curb	Cube	Coat
Card	Calm	Kay	Cost	Couch
Kiss	Café	Candle	Kettle	Copy
Canary	Kenny	Carpet	Cousin	Canoe

1. Have you bought your costume yet?
2. Please pass the ketchup.
3. That puppy is so cute!
4. Lat night I slept on a cot.
5. Batman has a cape.
6. His dad is a carpenter.
7. I need to curl my hair.
8. I heard a coyote last night.
9. Kim is a super teacher.
10. What color are your eyes?

Record below the dates of each Data Point (DP):
DP #1 _____ DP #2 _____ DP #3 _____ DP #4 _____ DP #5 _____ DP #6 _____

73

Student Name: _____ Grade: _____ Teacher/Tutor: _____

Directions: Teacher says each word or sentence aloud to student and student repeats. If student states the word incorrectly, teacher restates the word and student repeats once more. Practice on the target sound should take place at least 3 times per week for a period of no less than six weeks. Assessments should be given once a week throughout the implementation period.

Directions for giving assessments: Once a week use this sheet to asses the student's ability to pronounce the target sound. For each correct response place a '+' in the box below or adjacent to the word or sentence. For each incorrect response place a '–' in the box.

Articulation Drill Sheet
Focus Sound "K/C"

Medial 'K/C' Words:

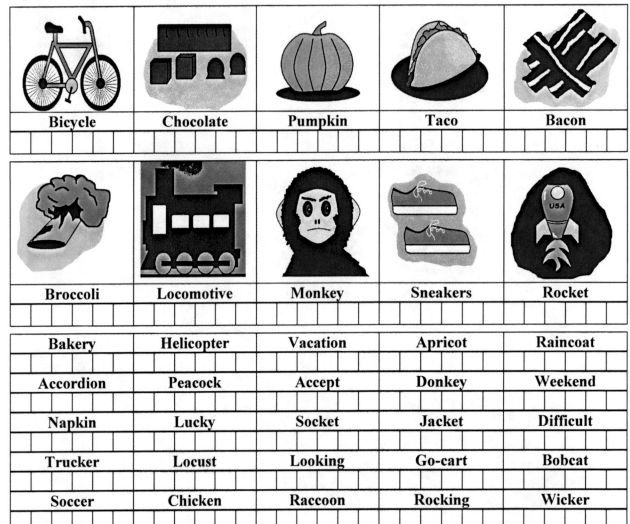

Bicycle	Chocolate	Pumpkin	Taco	Bacon

Broccoli	Locomotive	Monkey	Sneakers	Rocket

Bakery	Helicopter	Vacation	Apricot	Raincoat
Accordion	Peacock	Accept	Donkey	Weekend
Napkin	Lucky	Socket	Jacket	Difficult
Trucker	Locust	Looking	Go-cart	Bobcat
Soccer	Chicken	Raccoon	Rocking	Wicker

1. What's the occasion?
2. My favorite food is macaroni and cheese.
3. Please pass the barbeque sauce.
4. I hear you knocking on the door.
5. The bucket is full of water.
6. What is your mom cooking?
7. We eat turkey on Thanksgiving Day.
8. His uncle is a doctor.
9. The pelican caught a fish in its mouth.
10. She was a good speaker.

Record below the dates of each Data Point (DP):

DP #1 _____ DP #2 _____ DP #3 _____ DP #4 _____ DP #5 _____ DP #6 _____

Student Name: _____ Grade: _____ Teacher/Tutor: _____

Articulation Drill Sheet
Focus Sound "K/C"

Final 'K/C' Words:

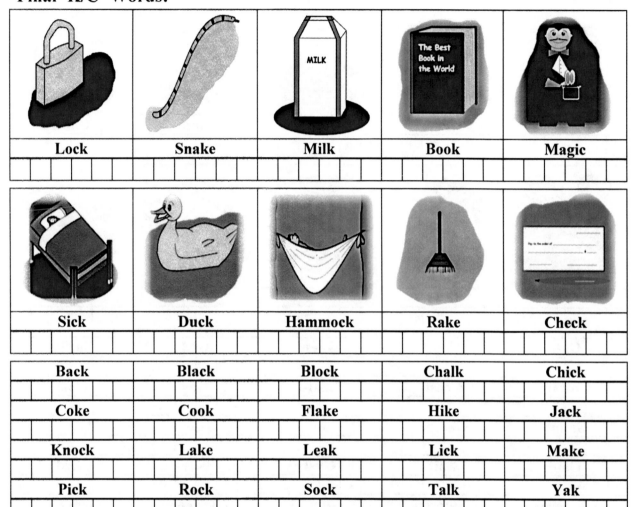

Lock	Snake	Milk	Book	Magic

Sick	Duck	Hammock	Rake	Check

Back	Black	Block	Chalk	Chick

Coke	Cook	Flake	Hike	Jack

Knock	Lake	Leak	Lick	Make

Pick	Rock	Sock	Talk	Yak

Lipstick	Snowflake	Toothache	Traffic	Rattlesnake

1. I want to eat a thick stea**k**.
2. We have a bri**ck** house.
3. Mi**k**e is getting married tomorrow.
4. Put on your cloa**k** before going outside.
5. He is the quarterba**ck** on the football team.
6. We need to cross the railroad tra**ck**.
7. Can you fix me a sna**ck**?
8. My mom will ba**k**e muffins.
9. I have to wa**k**e up very early tomorrow.
10. The decorations are in the atti**c**.

Record below the dates of each Data Point (DP):
DP #1 _____ DP #2 _____ DP #3 _____ DP #4 _____ DP #5 _____ DP #6 _____

Student Name: _____ Grade: _____ Teacher/Tutor: _____

Directions: Teacher says each word or sentence aloud to student and student repeats. If student states the word incorrectly, teacher restates the word and student repeats once more. Practice on the target sound should take place at least 3 times per week for a period of no less than six weeks. Assessments should be given once a week throughout the implementation period.

Directions for giving assessments: Once a week use this sheet to asses the student's ability to pronounce the target sound. For each correct response place a '+' in the box below or adjacent to the word or sentence. For each incorrect response place a '–' in the box.

Articulation Drill Sheet
Focus Sound "G"

Initial 'G' Words:

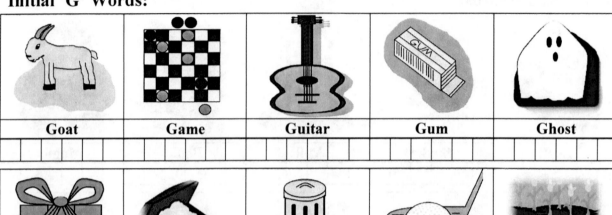

Goat	Game	Guitar	Gum	Ghost

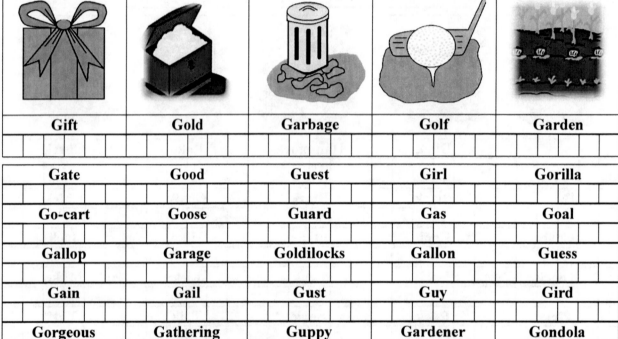

Gift	Gold	Garbage	Golf	Garden

Gate	Good	Guest	Girl	Gorilla

Go-cart	Goose	Guard	Gas	Goal

Gallop	Garage	Goldilocks	Gallon	Guess

Gain	Gail	Gust	Guy	Gird

Gorgeous	Gathering	Guppy	Gardener	Gondola

1. Gilbert broke his right arm.
2. The judge has a gavel.
3. Gazelles can run very fast.
4. She ripped her wedding gown.
5. You are giving me a headache.
6. Don't gobble your food.
7. She is in love with Gary.
8. Please bring me the garden hose.
9. The storm is in the Gulf of Mexico.
10. I love eating garlic bread.

Record below the dates of each Data Point (DP):

DP #1 _____ DP #2 _____ DP #3 _____ DP #4 _____ DP #5 _____ DP #6 _____

Student Name: _____ Grade: _____ Teacher/Tutor: _____

Articulation Drill Sheet
Focus Sound "G"

Medial 'G' Words:

Tiger	Igloo	Kangaroo	Tugboat	Cougar

Hamburger	Alligator	Spaghetti	Dragon	Sugar

Luggage	Jogging	Merry-go-round	Magazines	Mongoose
Sea gull	Again	Bagpipe	Bigger	Cigar
Dugout	Edgar	Jigsaw	Legal	Pigtail
Signal	Regard	Juggler	Wagon	Youngest
Fingernail	Marigold	Megaphone	Signature	Thanksgiving

1. Pick up the medicine at the drugstore.
2. School starts in August.
3. It was very foggy this morning.
4. The airport lost my luggage.
5. I miss my little doggy.
6. An elephant is bigger than a mouse.
7. Your room looks like a pigpen!
8. I have ten fingers.
9. She put the magnet on the refrigerator.
10. Look at the eagle in the sky!

Record below the dates of each Data Point (DP):
DP #1 _____ DP #2 _____ DP #3 _____ DP #4 _____ DP #5 _____ DP #6 _____

Student Name: _____ Grade: _____ Teacher/Tutor: _____

Directions: Teacher says each word or sentence aloud to student and student repeats. If student states the word incorrectly, teacher restates the word and student repeats once more. Practice on the target sound should take place at least 3 times per week for a period of no less than six weeks. Assessments should be given once a week throughout the implementation period.

Directions for giving assessments: Once a week use this sheet to asses the student's ability to pronounce the target sound. For each correct response place a '+' in the box below or adjacent to the word or sentence. For each incorrect response place a '−' in the box.

Articulation Drill Sheet
Focus Sound "G"

Final 'G' Words:

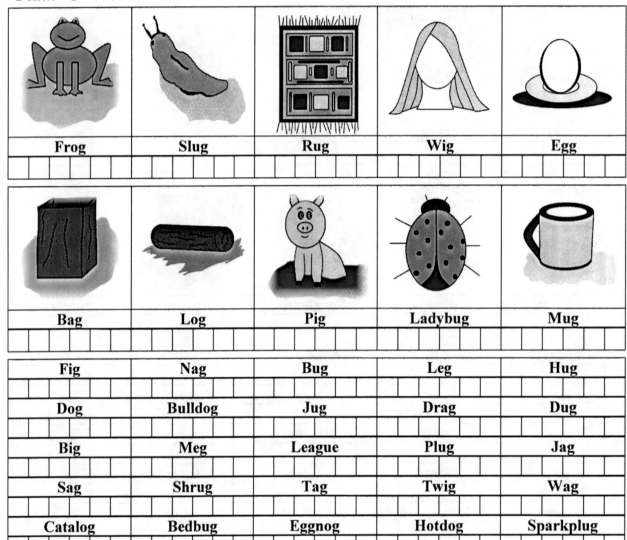

Frog	Slug	Rug	Wig	Egg
Bag	Log	Pig	Ladybug	Mug
Fig	Nag	Bug	Leg	Hug
Dog	Bulldog	Jug	Drag	Dug
Big	Meg	League	Plug	Jag
Sag	Shrug	Tag	Twig	Wag
Catalog	Bedbug	Eggnog	Hotdog	Sparkplug

1. Craig made the football team.
2. Let's play tug of war.
3. There is a lot of smog outside today.
4. Use a rag to wash the car.
5. Say the pledge to the flag.
6. Please put the peg in the pegboard.
7. That car belongs to Doug.
8. There is no need to brag.
9. The farmer fed the hog.
10. How far can you lug these books?

Record below the dates of each Data Point (DP):

DP #1 _____ DP #2 _____ DP #3 _____ DP #4 _____ DP #5 _____ DP #6 _____

Student Name: _____ Grade: _____ Teacher/Tutor: _____

Articulation Drill Sheet
Focus Sound "P"

Initial 'P' Words:

Pickles	Pear	Pumpkin	Peaches	Pig

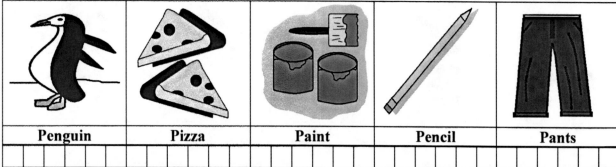

Penguin	Pizza	Paint	Pencil	Pants

Pet	Pal	Parrot	Party	Pearls

Parachute	Picnic	Piano	Puddle	Pie

Pirate	Pyramid	Poodle	Parade	Polar bear

Page	Pink	Penny	Pace	Park

Pigtail	Parakeet	Pineapple	Potato	Pajamas

1. There is a <u>p</u>ackage for me in the mailbox.
2. My mom put a <u>p</u>atch on my pants.
3. Please <u>p</u>ass the salt.
4. I want a <u>p</u>ony for my birthday.
5. Dad burnt the <u>p</u>opcorn.
6. John's dad is a <u>p</u>ilot.
7. She <u>p</u>aid me one hundred dollars.
8. The little boy drew a <u>p</u>icture for his mom.
9. <u>P</u>aul went hunting with me.
10. My <u>p</u>illow is so fluffy.

Record below the dates of each Data Point (DP):
DP #1 _____ DP #2 _____ DP #3 _____ DP #4 _____ DP #5 _____ DP #6 _____

Student Name: _____ Grade: _____ Teacher/Tutor: _____

Articulation Drill Sheet
Focus Sound "P"

Medial 'P' Words:

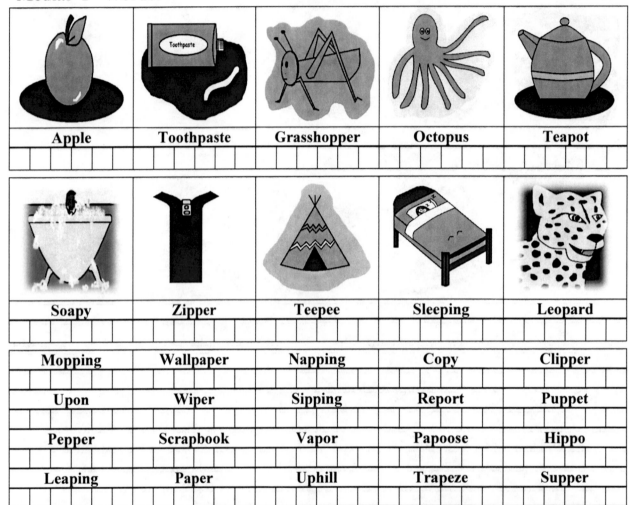

| Apple | Toothpaste | Grasshopper | Octopus | Teapot |

| Soapy | Zipper | Teepee | Sleeping | Leopard |

Mopping	Wallpaper	Napping	Copy	Clipper
Upon	Wiper	Sipping	Report	Puppet
Pepper	Scrapbook	Vapor	Papoose	Hippo
Leaping	Paper	Uphill	Trapeze	Supper
Diaper	Repair	Puppy	Japan	Coupon

1. I am so happy!
2. Will you bring me a napkin?
3. Mrs. Lopez is a great cook.
4. The faucet is dripping.
5. My uncle is chopping wood.
6. Please open your book to page four.
7. When I grow up I want to be a zookeeper.
8. She is a super student.
9. The rabbit is hopping.
10. What is your zip code?

Record below the dates of each Data Point (DP):
DP #1 _____ DP #2 _____ DP #3 _____ DP #4 _____ DP #5 _____ DP #6 _____

Student Name: _____ Grade: _____ Teacher/Tutor: _____

Directions: Teacher says each word or sentence aloud to student and student repeats. If student states the word incorrectly, teacher restates the word and student repeats once more. Practice on the target sound should take place at least 3 times per week for a period of no less than six weeks. Assessments should be given once a week throughout the implementation period.

Directions for giving assessments: Once a week use this sheet to asses the student's ability to pronounce the target sound. For each correct response place a '+' in the box below or adjacent to the word or sentence. For each incorrect response place a '−' in the box.

Articulation Drill Sheet
Focus Sound "P"

Final 'P' Words:

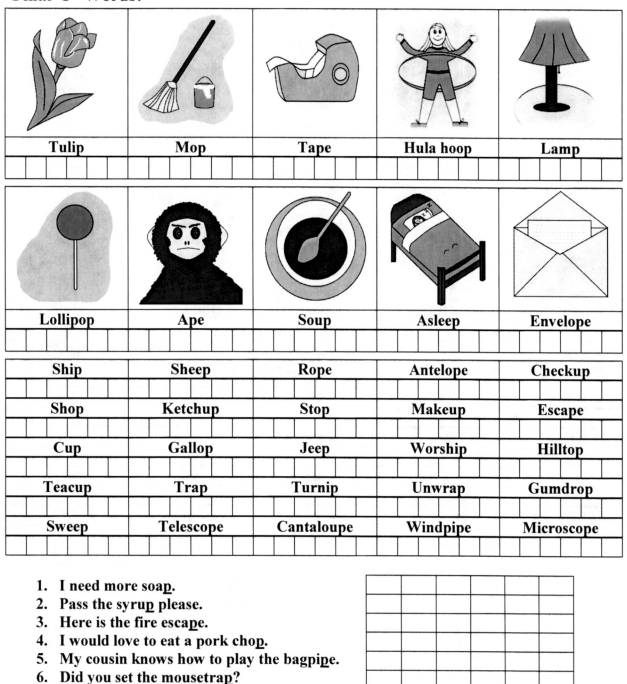

1. I need more soap.
2. Pass the syrup please.
3. Here is the fire escape.
4. I would love to eat a pork chop.
5. My cousin knows how to play the bagpipe.
6. Did you set the mousetrap?
7. His dad has a pickup truck.
8. I fell down the mountain slope.
9. Can you snap your fingers?
10. You sunk my battleship!

Record below the dates of each Data Point (DP):

DP #1 _____ DP #2 _____ DP #3 _____ DP #4 _____ DP #5 _____ DP #6 _____

81

Student Name: _____ Grade: _____ Teacher/Tutor: _____

Articulation Drill Sheet
Focus Sound "B"

Initial 'B' Words:

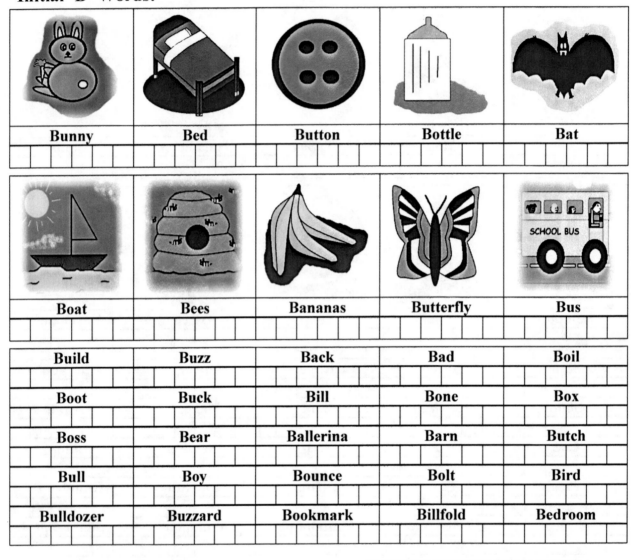

Bunny	Bed	Button	Bottle	Bat
Boat	Bees	Bananas	Butterfly	Bus
Build	Buzz	Back	Bad	Boil
Boot	Buck	Bill	Bone	Box
Boss	Bear	Ballerina	Barn	Butch
Bull	Boy	Bounce	Bolt	Bird
Bulldozer	Buzzard	Bookmark	Billfold	Bedroom

1. I always try to do my best.
2. She plays the drums in the rock band.
3. Betsy is the farmer's daughter.
4. There is candy in my Easter basket.
5. He ordered a baloney and cheese sandwich.
6. My dad knows how to play the banjo.
7. The basement is dark and scary.
8. The baby crawled across the floor.
9. Her behavior has improved.
10. We threw water balloons from the balcony.

Record below the dates of each Data Point (DP):
DP #1 _____ DP #2 _____ DP #3 _____ DP #4 _____ DP #5 _____ DP #6 _____

82

Student Name: _____ Grade: _____ Teacher/Tutor: _____

Directions: Teacher says each word or sentence aloud to student and student repeats. If student states the word incorrectly, teacher restates the word and student repeats once more. Practice on the target sound should take place at least 3 times per week for a period of no less than six weeks. Assessments should be given once a week throughout the implementation period.
Directions for giving assessments: Once a week use this sheet to asses the student's ability to pronounce the target sound. For each correct response place a '+' in the box below or adjacent to the word or sentence. For each incorrect response place a '−' in the box.

Articulation Drill Sheet
Focus Sound "B"

Medial 'B' Words:

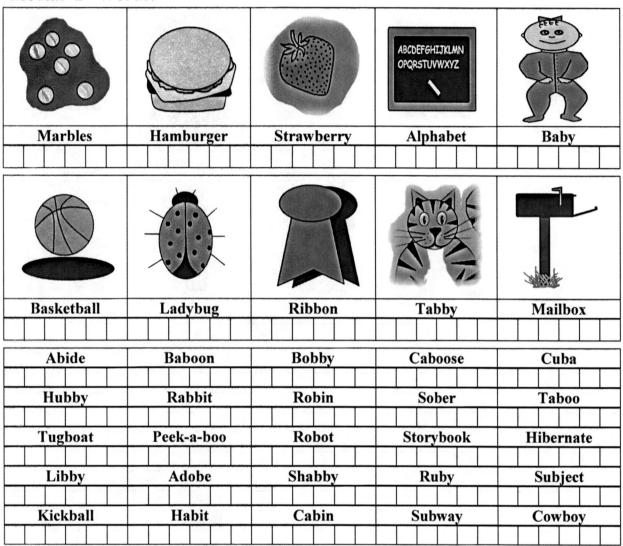

| Marbles | Hamburger | Strawberry | Alphabet | Baby |

| Basketball | Ladybug | Ribbon | Tabby | Mailbox |

Abide	Baboon	Bobby	Caboose	Cuba
Hubby	Rabbit	Robin	Sober	Taboo
Tugboat	Peek-a-boo	Robot	Storybook	Hibernate
Libby	Adobe	Shabby	Ruby	Subject
Kickball	Habit	Cabin	Subway	Cowboy

1. Halloween is in October.
2. Robert always makes me laugh.
3. We live in a great neighborhood.
4. I saw lots of acrobats at the circus.
5. My dad has a strong backbone.
6. I always hate saying goodbye.
7. Do you have a bobby pin?
8. She always rings a cowbell at the game.
9. Mabel lives near the ocean.
10. September is my favorite month.

Record below the dates of each Data Point (DP):
DP #1 _____ DP #2 _____ DP #3 _____ DP #4 _____ DP #5 _____ DP #6 _____

Student Name: _____ Grade: _____ Teacher/Tutor: _____

Articulation Drill Sheet
Focus Sound "B"

Final 'B' Words:

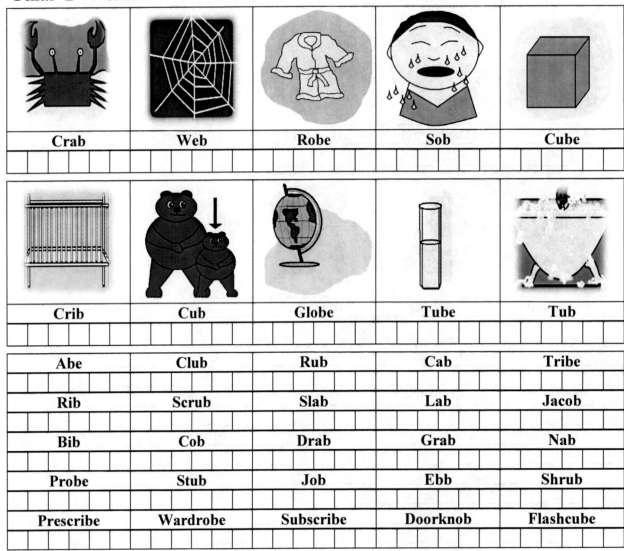

Crab	Web	Robe	Sob	Cube

Crib	Cub	Globe	Tube	Tub

Abe	Club	Rub	Cab	Tribe
Rib	Scrub	Slab	Lab	Jacob
Bib	Cob	Drab	Grab	Nab
Probe	Stub	Job	Ebb	Shrub
Prescribe	Wardrobe	Subscribe	Doorknob	Flashcube

1. Ro<u>b</u> is always late for school.
2. Yesterday we had a su<u>b</u> at school.
3. Dab a little on the cotton swa<u>b</u>.
4. There is a cobwe<u>b</u> in the corner.
5. I need a backru<u>b</u>.
6. Let's invite Bo<u>b</u> to the party.
7. Ga<u>b</u>e is a good student.
8. The mo<u>b</u> broke the law.
9. That woman is such a sno<u>b</u>.
10. My mom says my dad is a slo<u>b</u>.

Record below the dates of each Data Point (DP):
DP #1 _____   DP #2 _____   DP #3 _____   DP #4 _____   DP #5 _____   DP #6 _____

Student Name: _____ Grade: _____ Teacher/Tutor: _____

Articulation Drill Sheet
Focus Sound "T"

Initial 'T' Words:

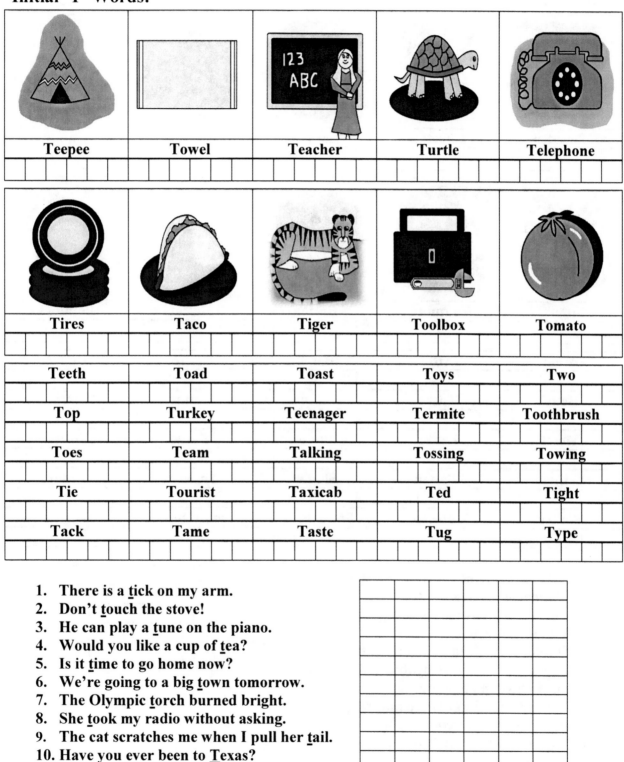

Teepee	Towel	Teacher	Turtle	Telephone

Tires	Taco	Tiger	Toolbox	Tomato

Teeth	Toad	Toast	Toys	Two

Top	Turkey	Teenager	Termite	Toothbrush

Toes	Team	Talking	Tossing	Towing

Tie	Tourist	Taxicab	Ted	Tight

Tack	Tame	Taste	Tug	Type

1. There is a tick on my arm.
2. Don't touch the stove!
3. He can play a tune on the piano.
4. Would you like a cup of tea?
5. Is it time to go home now?
6. We're going to a big town tomorrow.
7. The Olympic torch burned bright.
8. She took my radio without asking.
9. The cat scratches me when I pull her tail.
10. Have you ever been to Texas?

Record below the dates of each Data Point (DP):
DP #1 _____ DP #2 _____ DP #3 _____ DP #4 _____ DP #5 _____ DP #6 _____

Student Name: _____ Grade: _____ Teacher/Tutor: _____

Directions: Teacher says each word or sentence aloud to student and student repeats. If student states the word incorrectly, teacher restates the word and student repeats once more. Practice on the target sound should take place at least 3 times per week for a period of no less than six weeks. Assessments should be given once a week throughout the implementation period.

Directions for giving assessments: Once a week use this sheet to asses the student's ability to pronounce the target sound. For each correct response place a '+' in the box below or adjacent to the word or sentence. For each incorrect response place a '−' in the box.

Articulation Drill Sheet
Focus Sound "T"

Medial 'T' Words:

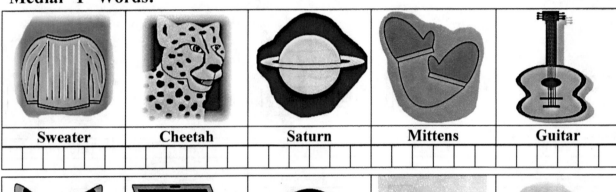

Sweater	Cheetah	Saturn	Mittens	Guitar

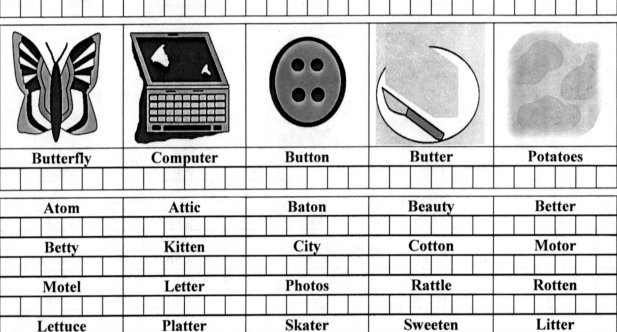

Butterfly	Computer	Button	Butter	Potatoes

Atom	Attic	Baton	Beauty	Better
Betty	Kitten	City	Cotton	Motor
Motel	Letter	Photos	Rattle	Rotten
Lettuce	Platter	Skater	Sweeten	Litter
Waiter	Anteater	Photograph	Peanut butter	Daughter

1. Let's go see a movie at the the<u>a</u>ter.
2. My teacher is in a mee<u>t</u>ing.
3. The dancer's dress is so pre<u>tt</u>y.
4. Vi<u>t</u>amins are good for you.
5. Jupi<u>t</u>er is the fifth planet from the sun.
6. I always have a good a<u>tt</u>itude.
7. She invi<u>t</u>ed me to her party.
8. My dad cuts the grass on Sa<u>t</u>urday.
9. His uncle was bitten by a ra<u>tt</u>lesnake.
10. We rode to the tenth floor on the eleva<u>t</u>or.

Record below the dates of each Data Point (DP):
DP #1 _____ DP #2 _____ DP #3 _____ DP #4 _____ DP #5 _____ DP #6 _____

Student Name: _____ Grade: _____ Teacher/Tutor: _____

Directions: Teacher says each word or sentence aloud to student and student repeats. If student states the word incorrectly, teacher restates the word and student repeats once more. Practice on the target sound should take place at least 3 times per week for a period of no less than six weeks. Assessments should be given once a week throughout the implementation period.

Directions for giving assessments: Once a week use this sheet to asses the student's ability to pronounce the target sound. For each correct response place a '+' in the box below or adjacent to the word or sentence. For each incorrect response place a '–' in the box.

Articulation Drill Sheet
Focus Sound "T"

Final 'T' Words:

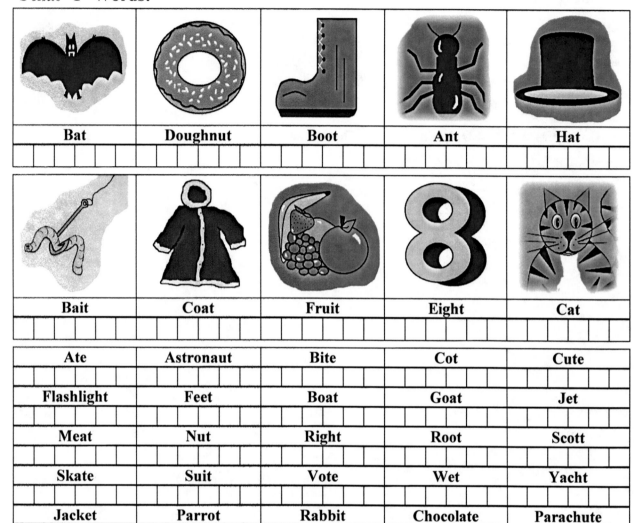

Bat	Doughnut	Boot	Ant	Hat

Bait	Coat	Fruit	Eight	Cat

Ate	Astronaut	Bite	Cot	Cute

Flashlight	Feet	Boat	Goat	Jet

Meat	Nut	Right	Root	Scott

Skate	Suit	Vote	Wet	Yacht

Jacket	Parrot	Rabbit	Chocolate	Parachute

1. My mom screamed when she saw a ra<u>t</u>.
2. Let's go fly a ki<u>t</u>e.
3. Ka<u>t</u>e is the mother of four sons.
4. My sister is going on a da<u>t</u>e tonight.
5. I have to si<u>t</u> still at school.
6. Tha<u>t</u> dog bit my arm.
7. It gets dark at nigh<u>t</u>.
8. Please go shu<u>t</u> the door.
9. We found a walle<u>t</u> on the sidewalk.
10. It gets ho<u>t</u> in the summertime.

Record below the dates of each Data Point (DP):
DP #1 _____ DP #2 _____ DP #3 _____ DP #4 _____ DP #5 _____ DP #6 _____

Student Name: _____ Grade: _____ Teacher/Tutor: _____

Articulation Drill Sheet
Focus Sound "D"

Initial 'D' Words:

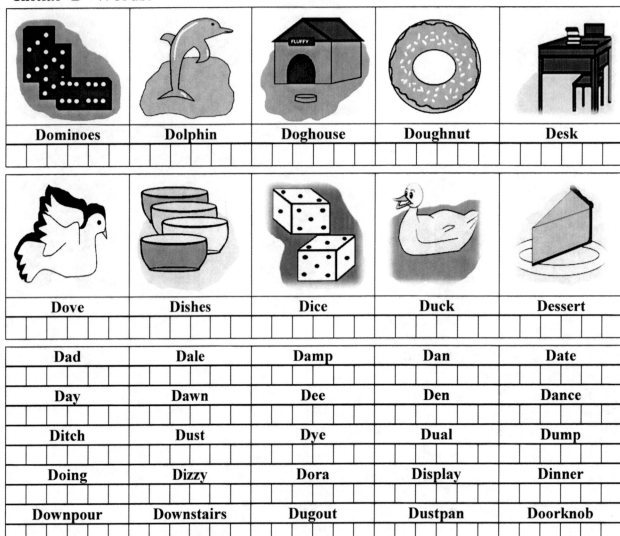

Dominoes	Dolphin	Doghouse	Doughnut	Desk

Dove	Dishes	Dice	Duck	Dessert

Dad	Dale	Damp	Dan	Date

Day	Dawn	Dee	Den	Dance

Ditch	Dust	Dye	Dual	Dump

Doing	Dizzy	Dora	Display	Dinner

Downpour	Downstairs	Dugout	Dustpan	Doorknob

1. My mom bought a dozen doughnuts.
2. I love to eat chips with onion dip.
3. My grandfather's boat is by the dock.
4. The doctor works in the hospital.
5. Dinah is my best friend.
6. The donkey ate my apple.
7. Her daughter is very pretty.
8. Please don't slam the door.
9. My brother loves to dive in the pool.
10. My baby sister has dimples on her face.

Record below the dates of each Data Point (DP):
DP #1 _____ DP #2 _____ DP #3 _____ DP #4 _____ DP #5 _____ DP #6 _____

Directions: Teacher says each word or sentence aloud to student and student repeats. If student states the word incorrectly, teacher restates the word and student repeats once more. Practice on the target sound should take place at least 3 times per week for a period of no less than six weeks. Assessments should be given once a week throughout the implementation period.

Directions for giving assessments: Once a week use this sheet to asses the student's ability to pronounce the target sound. For each correct response place a '+' in the box below or adjacent to the word or sentence. For each incorrect response place a '−' in the box.

Articulation Drill Sheet
Focus Sound "D"

Medial 'D' Words:

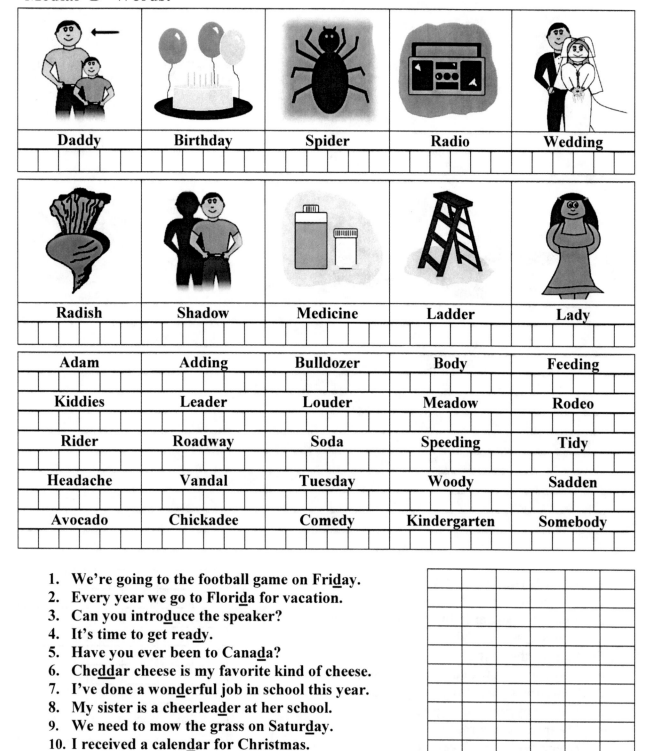

Daddy	Birthday	Spider	Radio	Wedding

Radish	Shadow	Medicine	Ladder	Lady

Adam	Adding	Bulldozer	Body	Feeding
Kiddies	Leader	Louder	Meadow	Rodeo
Rider	Roadway	Soda	Speeding	Tidy
Headache	Vandal	Tuesday	Woody	Sadden
Avocado	Chickadee	Comedy	Kindergarten	Somebody

1. We're going to the football game on Friday.
2. Every year we go to Florida for vacation.
3. Can you introduce the speaker?
4. It's time to get ready.
5. Have you ever been to Canada?
6. Cheddar cheese is my favorite kind of cheese.
7. I've done a wonderful job in school this year.
8. My sister is a cheerleader at her school.
9. We need to mow the grass on Saturday.
10. I received a calendar for Christmas.

Record below the dates of each Data Point (DP):

DP #1 _____ DP #2 _____ DP #3 _____ DP #4 _____ DP #5 _____ DP #6 _____

Student Name: _____ Grade: _____ Teacher/Tutor: _____

Directions: Teacher says each word or sentence aloud to student and student repeats. If student states the word incorrectly, teacher restates the word and student repeats once more. Practice on the target sound should take place at least 3 times per week for a period of no less than six weeks. Assessments should be given once a week throughout the implementation period.

Directions for giving assessments: Once a week use this sheet to asses the student's ability to pronounce the target sound. For each correct response place a '+' in the box below or adjacent to the word or sentence. For each incorrect response place a '–' in the box.

Articulation Drill Sheet
Focus Sound "D"

Final 'D' Words:

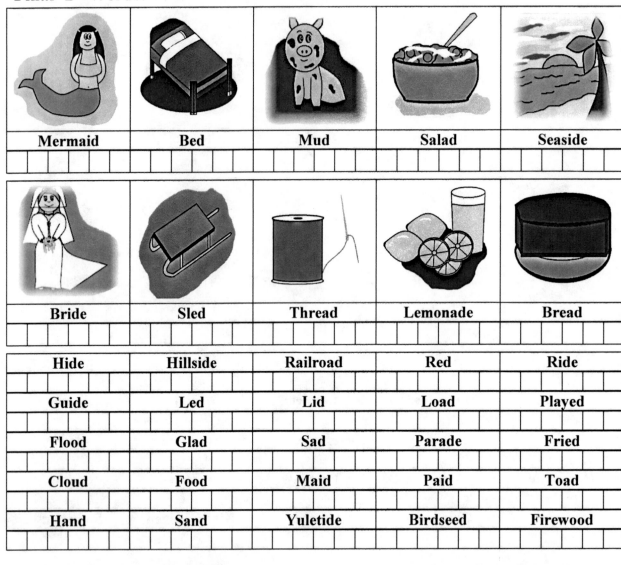

Mermaid	Bed	Mud	Salad	Seaside

Bride	Sled	Thread	Lemonade	Bread

Hide	Hillside	Railroad	Red	Ride
Guide	Led	Lid	Load	Played
Flood	Glad	Sad	Parade	Fried
Cloud	Food	Maid	Paid	Toad
Hand	Sand	Yuletide	Birdseed	Firewood

1. What is your zip code?
2. I want to succeed in school.
3. The squid swam to the bottom of the ocean.
4. A young boy can also be called a lad.
5. I am in the first grade this year.
6. Ned works at the supermarket every evening.
7. Sometimes we get too loud at school.
8. I saw a pyramid in Egypt.
9. My mom is in a really bad mood.
10. Every summer my cats shed.

Record below the dates of each Data Point (DP):
DP #1 _____ DP #2 _____ DP #3 _____ DP #4 _____ DP #5 _____ DP #6 _____

90

Student Name: _____ Grade: _____ Teacher/Tutor: _____

Directions: Teacher says each word or sentence aloud to student and student repeats. If student states the word incorrectly, teacher restates the word and student repeats once more. Practice on the target sound should take place at least 3 times per week for a period of no less than six weeks. Assessments should be given once a week throughout the implementation period.

Directions for giving assessments: Once a week use this sheet to asses the student's ability to pronounce the target sound. For each correct response place a '+' in the box below or adjacent to the word or sentence. For each incorrect response place a '–' in the box.

Articulation Drill Sheet
Focus Sound "J"

Initial 'J' Words:

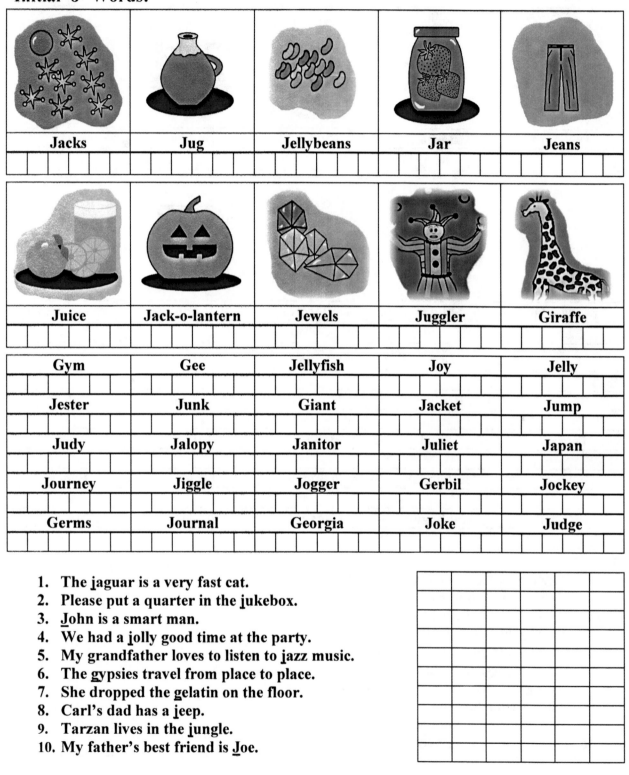

| | Jacks | Jug | Jellybeans | Jar | Jeans |

| | Juice | Jack-o-lantern | Jewels | Juggler | Giraffe |

Gym	Gee	Jellyfish	Joy	Jelly
Jester	Junk	Giant	Jacket	Jump
Judy	Jalopy	Janitor	Juliet	Japan
Journey	Jiggle	Jogger	Gerbil	Jockey
Germs	Journal	Georgia	Joke	Judge

1. The jaguar is a very fast cat.
2. Please put a quarter in the jukebox.
3. John is a smart man.
4. We had a jolly good time at the party.
5. My grandfather loves to listen to jazz music.
6. The gypsies travel from place to place.
7. She dropped the gelatin on the floor.
8. Carl's dad has a jeep.
9. Tarzan lives in the jungle.
10. My father's best friend is Joe.

Record below the dates of each Data Point (DP):
DP #1 _____ DP #2 _____ DP #3 _____ DP #4 _____ DP #5 _____ DP #6 _____

Student Name: _____ Grade: _____ Teacher/Tutor: _____

Directions: Teacher says each word or sentence aloud to student and student repeats. If student states the word incorrectly, teacher restates the word and student repeats once more. Practice on the target sound should take place at least 3 times per week for a period of no less than six weeks. Assessments should be given once a week throughout the implementation period.

Directions for giving assessments: Once a week use this sheet to asses the student's ability to pronounce the target sound. For each correct response place a '+' in the box below or adjacent to the word or sentence. For each incorrect response place a '–' in the box.

Articulation Drill Sheet
Focus Sound "J"

Medial 'J' Words:

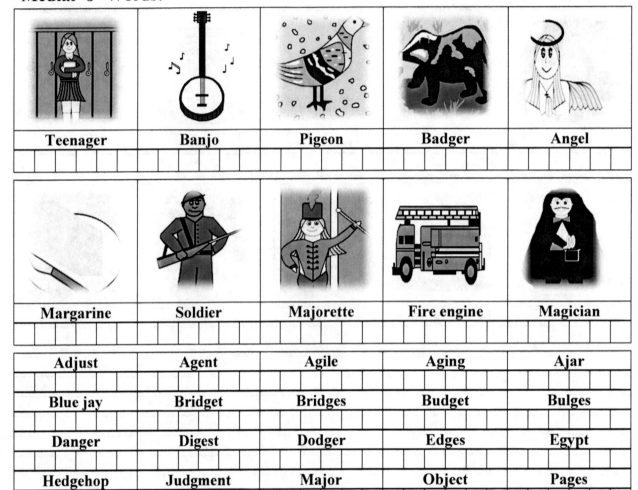

Teenager	Banjo	Pigeon	Badger	Angel

Margarine	Soldier	Majorette	Fire engine	Magician

Adjust	Agent	Agile	Aging	Ajar
Blue jay	Bridget	Bridges	Budget	Bulges
Danger	Digest	Dodger	Edges	Egypt
Hedgehop	Judgment	Major	Object	Pages
Angelfish	Cabbages	Magenta	Majesty	Objective

1. Roger is going to see the President.
2. My sister has to finish her project for school.
3. My sister won the beauty pageant.
4. It is urgent that we talk!
5. There is a legend on every map.
6. May I suggest something?
7. My algebra teacher just had a baby.
8. What is your favorite subject in school?
9. Nitrogen is a type of gas.
10. The stagecoach arrived on time.

Record below the dates of each Data Point (DP):

DP #1 _____ DP #2 _____ DP #3 _____ DP #4 _____ DP #5 _____ DP #6 _____

Directions: Teacher says each word or sentence aloud to student and student repeats. If student states the word incorrectly, teacher restates the word and student repeats once more. Practice on the target sound should take place at least 3 times per week for a period of no less than six weeks. Assessments should be given once a week throughout the implementation period.

Directions for giving assessments: Once a week use this sheet to asses the student's ability to pronounce the target sound. For each correct response place a '+' in the box below or adjacent to the word or sentence. For each incorrect response place a '−' in the box.

Articulation Drill Sheet
Focus Sound "J"

Final 'J' Words:

Garbage	Orange	Cabbage	Bridge	Postage

Cage	Fudge	Beverage	Luggage	Sponge

Badge	Change	Forge	Edge	Barge
Huge	Marge	Page	Ridge	Smudge
Bulge	Hedge	Wedge	Stage	Allege
Image	Large	Dosage	College	Mileage
Language	Foliage	Voyage	Advantage	Percentage

1. Our furniture is in storage.
2. Goldilocks ate my porridge.
3. Driving is a privilege.
4. My parents have a good marriage.
5. She has a bandage on her finger.
6. Marge is Homer's wife.
7. We have backstage tickets.
8. He has a cottage by the lake.
9. I ate a sausage biscuit for breakfast.
10. My dad sent me a message.

Record below the dates of each Data Point (DP):

DP #1 _____ DP #2 _____ DP #3 _____ DP #4 _____ DP #5 _____ DP #6 _____

Student Name: _____ Grade: _____ Teacher/Tutor: _____

Directions: Teacher says each word or sentence aloud to student and student repeats. If student states the word incorrectly, teacher restates the word and student repeats once more. Practice on the target sound should take place at least 3 times per week for a period of no less than six weeks. Assessments should be given once a week throughout the implementation period.
Directions for giving assessments: Once a week use this sheet to asses the student's ability to pronounce the target sound. For each correct response place a '+' in the box below or adjacent to the word or sentence. For each incorrect response place a '−' in the box.

Articulation Drill Sheet
Focus Sound "H"

Initial 'H' Words:

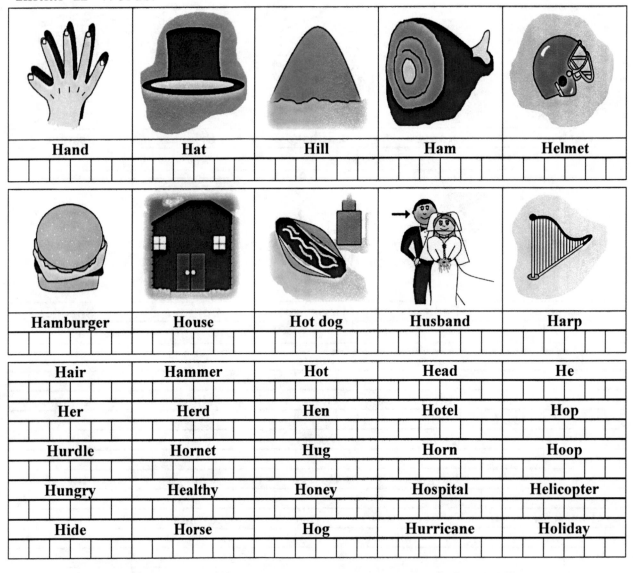

Hand	Hat	Hill	Ham	Helmet

Hamburger	House	Hot dog	Husband	Harp

Hair	Hammer	Hot	Head	He
Her	Herd	Hen	Hotel	Hop
Hurdle	Hornet	Hug	Horn	Hoop
Hungry	Healthy	Honey	Hospital	Helicopter
Hide	Horse	Hog	Hurricane	Holiday

1. My dad's name is <u>H</u>arvey.
2. <u>H</u>ang your coat on the <u>h</u>ook.
3. I <u>h</u>onked the <u>h</u>orn when the dog got out.
4. The <u>h</u>yenas ate a zebra.
5. You make me so <u>h</u>appy.
6. When the phone rings just say <u>h</u>ello.
7. I can count to one <u>h</u>undred.
8. The kitten was stuck in a <u>h</u>ole.
9. She <u>h</u>as a cool car!
10. <u>H</u>ummingbirds are very small birds.

Record below the dates of each Data Point (DP):
DP #1 _____ DP #2 _____ DP #3 _____ DP #4 _____ DP #5 _____ DP #6 _____

Student Name: _____ Grade: _____ Teacher/Tutor: _____

Directions: Teacher says each word or sentence aloud to student and student repeats. If student states the word incorrectly, teacher restates the word and student repeats once more. Practice on the target sound should take place at least 3 times per week for a period of no less than six weeks. Assessments should be given once a week throughout the implementation period.
Directions for giving assessments: Once a week use this sheet to asses the student's ability to pronounce the target sound. For each correct response place a '+' in the box below or adjacent to the word or sentence. For each incorrect response place a '−' in the box.

Articulation Drill Sheet
Focus Sound "H"

Medial 'H' Words:

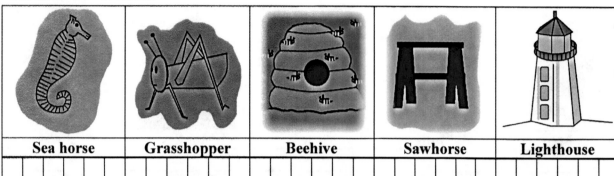

| Sea horse | Grasshopper | Beehive | Sawhorse | Lighthouse |

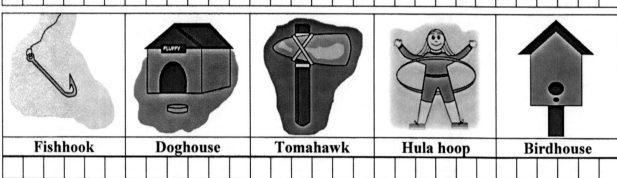

| Fishhook | Doghouse | Tomahawk | Hula hoop | Birdhouse |

Buttonhole	Rocking horse	Uphill	Downhill	Behave
Rehearse	Pothole	Ahead	Study hall	Anyhow
Keyhole	Manhole	Playhouse	Forehead	Greenhouse
Redhead	Bellhop	High heels	Hitchhike	Potholder
Clothes hanger	O'Hara	Unhappy	Behavior	Abraham

1. The president lives in the White <u>H</u>ouse.
2. My uncle lives in O<u>h</u>io.
3. I put my book in my cubby <u>h</u>ole.
4. The policewoman will appre<u>h</u>end the thief.
5. Ground<u>h</u>ogs love to dig holes.
6. She was a sight to be<u>h</u>old!
7. We have a tree<u>h</u>ouse in the back yard.
8. Please un<u>h</u>ook the buckle.
9. He ran so much he became de<u>h</u>ydrated.
10. Captain <u>H</u>ook is a scary man!

Record below the dates of each Data Point (DP):
DP #1 _____ DP #2 _____ DP #3 _____ DP #4 _____ DP #5 _____ DP #6 _____

95

Articulation Drill Sheet
Focus Sound "M"

Initial 'M' Words:

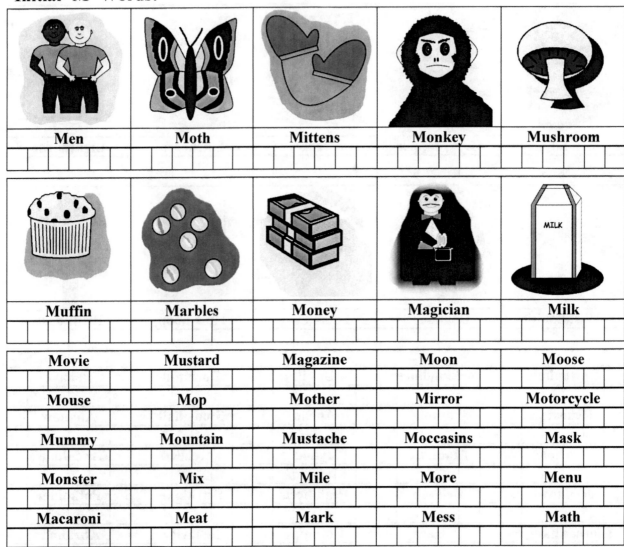

Men	Moth	Mittens	Monkey	Mushroom

Muffin	Marbles	Money	Magician	Milk

Movie	Mustard	Magazine	Moon	Moose
Mouse	**Mop**	**Mother**	**Mirror**	**Motorcycle**
Mummy	**Mountain**	**Mustache**	**Moccasins**	**Mask**
Monster	**Mix**	**Mile**	**More**	**Menu**
Macaroni	**Meat**	**Mark**	**Mess**	**Math**

1. He tore up <u>my</u> paper!
2. We always go shopping on <u>M</u>onday.
3. <u>My</u> dad is the <u>m</u>anager at the restaurant.
4. <u>My</u> sister tracked <u>m</u>ud on the new carpet.
5. <u>My</u> big brother is <u>m</u>oving out today.
6. She named her baby <u>M</u>ike.
7. <u>My</u> <u>m</u>om bought a new <u>m</u>attress for <u>my</u> bed.
8. We used a <u>m</u>ap to travel to Florida.
9. <u>My</u> cousin is from <u>M</u>ontana.
10. <u>My</u> dad has big <u>m</u>uscles.

Record below the dates of each Data Point (DP):
DP #1 _____   DP #2 _____   DP #3 _____   DP #4 _____   DP #5 _____   DP #6 _____

Directions: Teacher says each word or sentence aloud to student and student repeats. If student states the word incorrectly, teacher restates the word and student repeats once more. Practice on the target sound should take place at least 3 times per week for a period of no less than six weeks. Assessments should be given once a week throughout the implementation period.

Directions for giving assessments: Once a week use this sheet to asses the student's ability to pronounce the target sound. For each correct response place a '+' in the box below or adjacent to the word or sentence. For each incorrect response place a '–' in the box.

Articulation Drill Sheet
Focus Sound "M"

Medial 'M' Words:

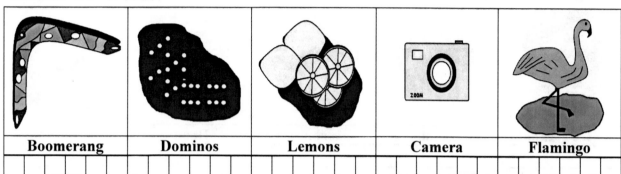

Boomerang	Dominos	Lemons	Camera	Flamingo

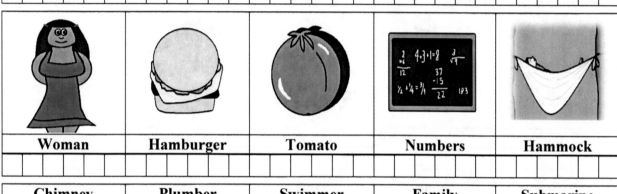

Woman	Hamburger	Tomato	Numbers	Hammock

Chimney	Plumber	Swimmer	Family	Submarine

Drummer	Lawnmower	Customer	Amount	Almost

Cement	Blooming	Cinnamon	Hammer	Comedy

Limited	Salami	Shoemaker	Wyoming	Chameleon

Camel	Tomcat	Tammy	Limit	Memorize

1. It gets hot in the summer.
2. My sister has asthma.
3. One day I'll be a famous singer.
4. The state of Georgia is next to Alabama.
5. Can someone help me?
6. He has a good sense of humor.
7. The gymnast did a somersault.
8. I am proud to be an American.
9. We wash our clothes at the Laundromat.
10. I won first place at the tournament.

Record below the dates of each Data Point (DP):

DP #1 _____ DP #2 _____ DP #3 _____ DP #4 _____ DP #5 _____ DP #6 _____

Student Name: _____ Grade: _____ Teacher/Tutor: _____

Directions: Teacher says each word or sentence aloud to student and student repeats. If student states the word incorrectly, teacher restates the word and student repeats once more. Practice on the target sound should take place at least 3 times per week for a period of no less than six weeks. Assessments should be given once a week throughout the implementation period.

Directions for giving assessments: Once a week use this sheet to asses the student's ability to pronounce the target sound. For each correct response place a '+' in the box below or adjacent to the word or sentence. For each incorrect response place a '−' in the box.

Articulation Drill Sheet
Focus Sound "M"

Final 'M' Words:

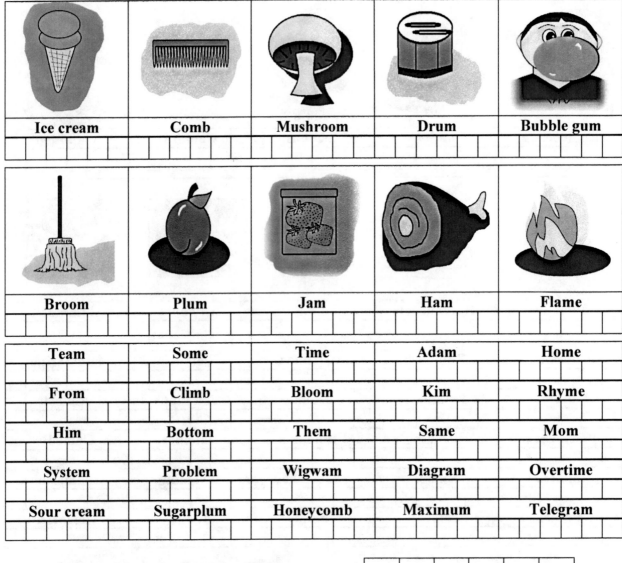

Ice cream	Comb	Mushroom	Drum	Bubble gum

Broom	Plum	Jam	Ham	Flame

Team	Some	Time	Adam	Home

From	Climb	Bloom	Kim	Rhyme

Him	Bottom	Them	Same	Mom

System	Problem	Wigwam	Diagram	Overtime

Sour cream	Sugarplum	Honeycomb	Maximum	Telegram

1. Flowers bloom in the springtime.
2. Abraham brought his lunch today.
3. May I please go to the bathroom?
4. The caterpillar crawled out on a limb.
5. Can you loan me a dime?
6. I got a denim jacket for my birthday.
7. Will you read me a bedtime story?
8. Hopscotch is my favorite game.
9. You must remain calm.
10. What is your name?

Record below the dates of each Data Point (DP):
DP #1 _____ DP #2 _____ DP #3 _____ DP #4 _____ DP #5 _____ DP #6 _____

Student Name: _____ Grade: _____ Teacher/Tutor: _____

Articulation Drill Sheet
Focus Sound "N"

Initial 'N' Words:

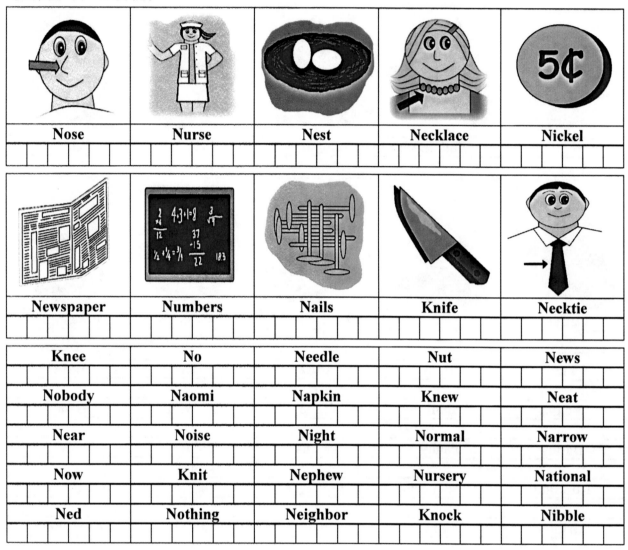

Nose	Nurse	Nest	Necklace	Nickel

Newspaper	Numbers	Nails	Knife	Necktie

Knee	No	Needle	Nut	News
Nobody	Naomi	Napkin	Knew	Neat
Near	Noise	Night	Normal	Narrow
Now	Knit	Nephew	Nursery	National
Ned	Nothing	Neighbor	Knock	Nibble

1. I love the month of <u>N</u>ovember.
2. My <u>n</u>iece is from Texas.
3. Have you ever been to <u>N</u>ebraska?
4. I went to see the ballet 'The <u>N</u>utcracker'.
5. She has a crick in her <u>n</u>eck.
6. My mom sleeps in a <u>n</u>ightgown.
7. <u>N</u>icky hit a home run.
8. Those kids are <u>n</u>oisy!
9. That is a <u>n</u>utritious meal.
10. Happy <u>N</u>ew Year!

Record below the dates of each Data Point (DP):
DP #1 _____ DP #2 _____ DP #3 _____ DP #4 _____ DP #5 _____ DP #6 _____

Student Name: _____ Grade: _____ Teacher/Tutor: _____

Directions: Teacher says each word or sentence aloud to student and student repeats. If student states the word incorrectly, teacher restates the word and student repeats once more. Practice on the target sound should take place at least 3 times per week for a period of no less than six weeks. Assessments should be given once a week throughout the implementation period.

Directions for giving assessments: Once a week use this sheet to asses the student's ability to pronounce the target sound. For each correct response place a '+' in the box below or adjacent to the word or sentence. For each incorrect response place a '−' in the box.

Articulation Drill Sheet
Focus Sound "N"

Medial 'N' Words:

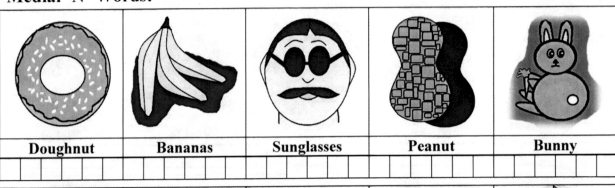

| Doughnut | Bananas | Sunglasses | Peanut | Bunny |

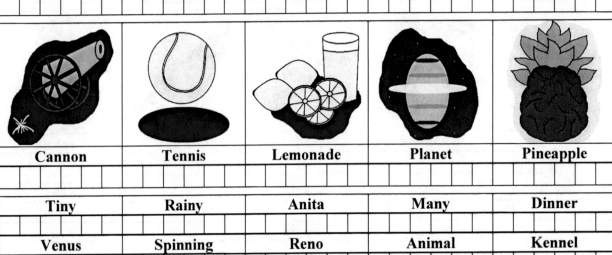

| Cannon | Tennis | Lemonade | Planet | Pineapple |

Tiny	Rainy	Anita	Many	Dinner
Venus	Spinning	Reno	Animal	Kennel
Danny	Penny	Bonus	Honey	Chimney
Running	Honeybee	Teenager	Volcano	Beginner
Airliner	Weiner	Pony	Another	Cinnamon

1. Today is a su<u>nn</u>y day.
2. Everyone is a wi<u>nn</u>er!
3. My grandmother has a yellow ca<u>n</u>ary.
4. The u<u>n</u>iverse is very big.
5. We went down the river in a ca<u>n</u>oe.
6. Do you have a<u>n</u>y more gum?
7. My father sings te<u>n</u>or at church.
8. I love to draw di<u>n</u>osaurs.
9. My dad bought a new law<u>n</u>mower.
10. That man is very ge<u>n</u>erous.

Record below the dates of each Data Point (DP):
DP #1 _____ DP #2 _____ DP #3 _____ DP #4 _____ DP #5 _____ DP #6 _____

Directions: Teacher says each word or sentence aloud to student and student repeats. If student states the word incorrectly, teacher restates the word and student repeats once more. Practice on the target sound should take place at least 3 times per week for a period of no less than six weeks. Assessments should be given once a week throughout the implementation period.

Directions for giving assessments: Once a week use this sheet to asses the student's ability to pronounce the target sound. For each correct response place a '+' in the box below or adjacent to the word or sentence. For each incorrect response place a '−' in the box.

Articulation Drill Sheet
Focus Sound "N"

Final 'N' Words:

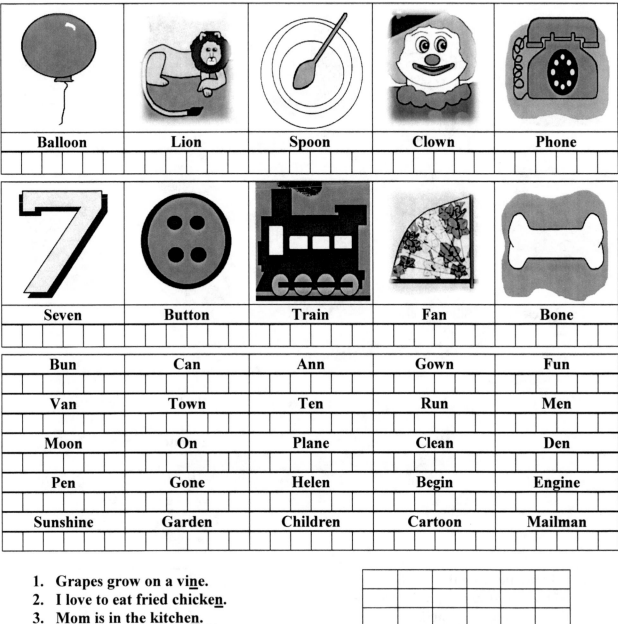

1. Grapes grow on a vine.
2. I love to eat fried chicken.
3. Mom is in the kitchen.
4. Have you seen my purse?
5. When will dad be home?
6. The king wears a crown.
7. The water fountain is broken.
8. She is scared to go in that house.
9. My brother is down stairs.
10. That dog has a chain around its neck.

Record below the dates of each Data Point (DP):

DP #1 _____ DP #2 _____ DP #3 _____ DP #4 _____ DP #5 _____ DP #6 _____

Student Name: _____ Grade: _____ Teacher/Tutor: _____

Directions: Teacher says each word or sentence aloud to student and student repeats. If student states the word incorrectly, teacher restates the word and student repeats once more. Practice on the target sound should take place at least 3 times per week for a period of no less than six weeks. Assessments should be given once a week throughout the implementation period.

Directions for giving assessments: Once a week use this sheet to asses the student's ability to pronounce the target sound. For each correct response place a '+' in the box below or adjacent to the word or sentence. For each incorrect response place a '−' in the box.

Articulation Drill Sheet
Focus Sound "Y"

Initial 'Y' Words:

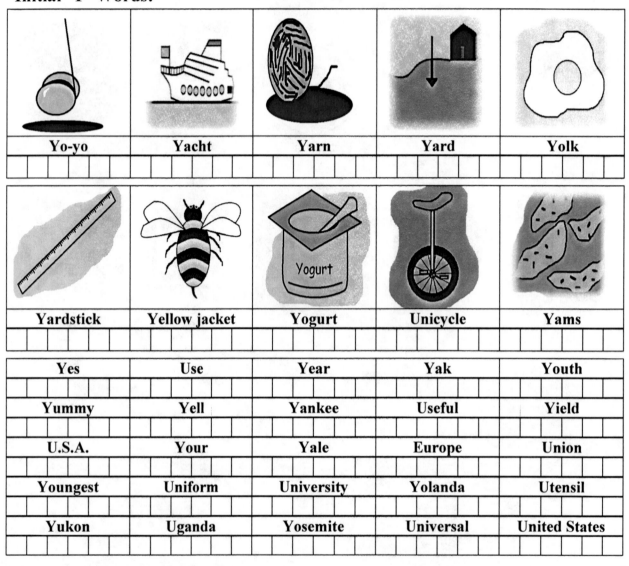

Yo-yo	Yacht	Yarn	Yard	Yolk

Yardstick	Yellow jacket	Yogurt	Unicycle	Yams

Yes	Use	Year	Yak	Youth
Yummy	Yell	Yankee	Useful	Yield
U.S.A.	Your	Yale	Europe	Union
Youngest	Uniform	University	Yolanda	Utensil
Yukon	Uganda	Yosemite	Universal	United States

1. My picture is in the yearbook.
2. Have you seen my yellow sweater?
3. She is using my pencil.
4. Some people believe in unicorns.
5. We went to the movies yesterday.
6. My parents belong to the yacht club.
7. You can tie your shoes by yourself.
8. My brother is younger than me.
9. Do you like to eat yams?
10. Stop yelling at me!

Record below the dates of each Data Point (DP):

DP #1 _____ DP #2 _____ DP #3 _____ DP #4 _____ DP #5 _____ DP #6 _____

Directions: Teacher says each word or sentence aloud to student and student repeats. If student states the word incorrectly, teacher restates the word and student repeats once more. Practice on the target sound should take place at least 3 times per week for a period of no less than six weeks. Assessments should be given once a week throughout the implementation period.

Directions for giving assessments: Once a week use this sheet to asses the student's ability to pronounce the target sound. For each correct response place a '+' in the box below or adjacent to the word or sentence. For each incorrect response place a '−' in the box.

Articulation Drill Sheet
Focus Sound "Y"

Medial 'Y' Words:

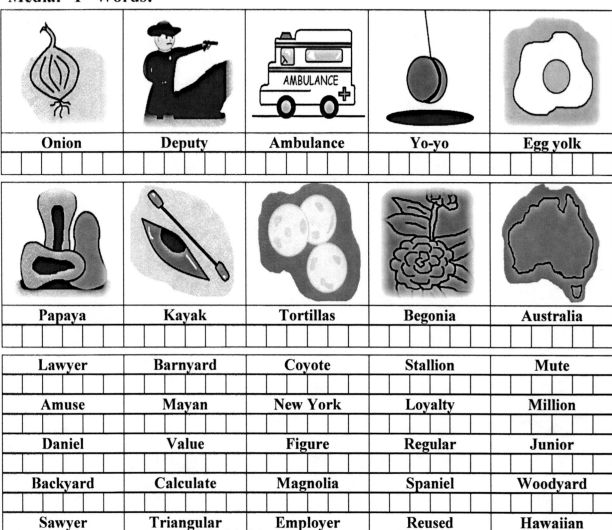

Onion	Deputy	Ambulance	Yo-yo	Egg yolk

Papaya	Kayak	Tortillas	Begonia	Australia

Lawyer	Barnyard	Coyote	Stallion	Mute
Amuse	Mayan	New York	Loyalty	Million
Daniel	Value	Figure	Regular	Junior
Backyard	Calculate	Magnolia	Spaniel	Woodyard
Sawyer	Triangular	Employer	Reused	Hawaiian

1. Last year I went to the Grand Canyon.
2. My grandfather's name is William.
3. He looks familiar to me.
4. I've always wanted to go to New York City.
5. Donald Trump is a billionaire.
6. Amelia works at the grocery store.
7. He gave the book to Maya.
8. She lives down in the bayou.
9. My mom has a lot of azaleas in her yard.
10. My favorite color is royal blue.

Record below the dates of each Data Point (DP):
DP #1 _____ DP #2 _____ DP #3 _____ DP #4 _____ DP #5 _____ DP #6 _____

CPSIA information can be obtained
at www.ICGtesting.com
Printed in the USA
LVOW09s0825040618

579484LV00004B/165/P

9 780578 003214